Trust and Understanding

the person-centred approach to
everyday care for people
with special needs

second edition

Marlis Pörtner

PCCS BOOKS
Ross-on-Wye

PCCS BOOKS
2 Cropper Row
Alton Road
ROSS-ON-WYE
HR9 5LA
UK
Tel +44 (0)1989 763900

www.pccs-books.co.uk

This revised and extended edition published 2007

Ernstnehmen – Zutrauen – Verstehen
by Marlis Pörtner
Klett-Cotta
© 1996, 2004 J.G. Cotta'sche Buchhandlung Nachfolger GmbH
Stuttgart

For the English language translation:
© 2000, Marlis Pörtner
© 2006, revised and extended, Marlis Pörtner

Trust and Understanding
the person-centred approach to everyday care
for people with special needs

ISBN 978-1-898-05991-2

Cover design by Denis Postle.
Printed by Cromwell Press, Trowbridge, UK

Contents

Figures and Signposts

Some comments on the second edition

The widespread recognition of the original German edition of this book has brought new experiences, encounters and insights. Most of them I described in a new book *Brücken bauen* (2003) (Building Bridges). Others resulted in modifications and additions for the fourth German edition (2004), which are now included in this second English edition. However, in its substance, the book remains unchanged.

The keyword lists of the main criteria of the concept, which I use in training workshops, have also proved to be useful for team meetings, supervision or case-work, as well as for individual reflection. These lists, serving as 'Signposts', are part of the book now. 'Guidelines for everyday work' have been completed with a new criterion, which in practice, again and again, proves to be crucial: 'Not constantly staring at the symptom'.

The growing interest in the person-centred approach among managers of social organisations has led to some additional considerations about the concept as a management instrument and about its implications for management functions, thus, creating an extended chapter, 'The status of the person-centred concept within organisations'.

Acknowledgements

My deep gratitude goes to all those who have, in various ways, contributed to this book: to the persons whom I have had the privilege to work with all these years—in training, consultation, supervision or psychotherapy—and who in inestimable ways have helped me to broaden my horizons of understanding. They have all played their part in the development and shaping of the ideas presented here.

Sincere thanks to Sigrid Baumann, Ursula Friedrich, Harry Hulskers, Barbara Krietemeyer, Petr Ondracek, Rini Schenck, Maria Schmucki, Cécile Schwarz, Angela Turner, Allan Turner and Dion Van Werde for informative conversations related to the subject of this book and for kindly contributing examples from their own professional or personal experience.

My special thanks to Garry Prouty, who was the first person to encourage me to write this book and whose concepts have confirmed, as well as inspired, my own ideas.

With the publication of this new, revised, English edition sincere thanks go to all those—trainers, lecturers, managers of organisations and carers—who, since the book's first publication, have contributed in spreading the ideas it stands for, have picked up my suggestions and are transferring them into their daily work.

I thank the two organisations who started to consistently work with the concept of 'Trust and Understanding': the Arbeiter-Samariter-Bund Bremen (ASB), Germany, and the Stiftung für Schwerbehinderte Luzern (SSBL), Switzerland. My sincere thanks to those responsible: Jürgen Lehmann, Konrad Seidl, Heinz Becker and the project group at the ASB: Stephan Bachmann, Dani Hohler and the members of the management at the SSBL, as well as to the entire staff of both organisations for their commitment to work on the basis of this concept. All of them achieve invaluable pioneering work.

I am indebted to all staff members of the editorial, production and marketing departments at Klett-Cotta's, my German publisher, who contributed to the publication of the original German book, that in 2006 has reached its fifth edition.

I thank Elke Lambers for recommending the book to PCCS Books and Alexandra Szigeti for helpful advice with the translation. And last, but not least, I want to express my most sincere esteem and gratitude to Maggie Taylor-Sanders and Pete Sanders for making my concepts available to English readers, and to particularly thank Maggie for her sensible and sensitive editing. PCCS Books' willingness to foster the mutuality of exchanging ideas and knowledge between the languages is exemplary and pioneering and deserves deep appreciation and respect.

Zurich, Switzerland, December 2006.

1
Introduction

The idea for writing this book emerged from many years of consulting staff members of different communities and institutions, as well as from my therapeutic work with people with special needs. More and more I realised how much the person-centred approach has to offer in this field. Moreover, to my surprise, I saw it happen more than once that carers, without having a specific knowledge of the person-centred approach, intuitively developed ways to work which were quite close to its principles. It seemed as if the experience of getting stuck with what has been tried before, would sometimes lead quite naturally to ways which embrace trust and understanding and offer others more space to take their own initiative and responsibility. These promising approaches mark points where we can begin.

Concrete examples will illustrate what it means to work in a person-centred way, in different fields and according to different tasks and circumstances. Person-centred work in other fields is not the same as client-centred psychotherapy. To make this very clear was another motivation to write this book, as so many misunderstandings and misjudgements of the person-centred approach result from not paying sufficient attention to this differentiation.

This may be one of the reasons why a consistent person-centred attitude and a solid knowledge of its fundamentals are only very rarely the basis of work in a social institution. Yet the person-centred philosophy is highly suitable to meet the specific requirements of this field. Working on its principles is likely to:
- improve life quality for the people taken care of
- extend their frame of action
- facilitate the staff's work
- diminish the negative effects of frequently changing staff
- counterbalance burn-out symptoms.

Therefore it might be useful to establish a concept which makes explicit what it actually means to work in a person-centred way, and to develop guidelines which help to implement it in everyday work for people with special needs or in need of care. The concept, though, is not restricted to just these areas. Its principles can be suitably adapted to other fields and modified to fit other tasks and circumstances. However, in this book the fundamentals of person-centred work are illustrated mainly by examples from working with adults with special needs; not only because I have the most experience in this field, but also because I feel that with them what is essential when working with human beings becomes particularly visible—as through a looking glass. In addition some other examples from my consulting experience, or reported by colleagues, will demonstrate how the same principles work equally well in other fields. Names and some details have been changed in order to respect the anonymity of the people described. The variety of examples is meant to encourage the reader's own considerations about how to work in a person-centred way in their own professional field.

The use of language in this book

I completely agree with, and support, every effort to avoid disparaging terms and use a language which respects the human dignity and integrity of people with special needs, and I fully understand their concern and sensitivity about being labelled in a derogatory way. Yet, very frequently, it is not the language itself which is disrespecting, but the attitude with which it is used. This attitude behind the words is perceived by people with special needs. As long as the attitude does not change, changing the words will have only a very limited effect.

It goes without saying that we have to be particularly careful not to use terms which in themselves are disparaging (like 'cripple' or 'idiot', which were used in the past). But what we see now is how one word after another is rejected as disrespectful and consequently the language becomes impoverished to a point where it can no longer adequately express the complexity of the subject, but is reduced to simplification which in no way does justice to people with special needs. The term 'people with special needs' is very helpful as a general expression, but not suitable in every specific context and sometimes linguistically not correct. 'Learning disabilities' is a very specific notion, grasping only one part of the problem, but not covering the complexity we have to cope with. Although it is true that people with special needs, as a rule, have learning disabilities, there is, on the other hand, a large number of people with learning disabilities who don't have, in any way, the 'special needs' we are dealing with here. In German we have different words, but similar problems. The British author Valerie Sinason,[1] in a very informative and relevant chapter 'Euphemisms and Abuse', describes these problems and their historical roots.

It is necessary to look more carefully at the real meaning of the words we use, in order to make sure that they are not disparaging and, at the same time, suitable to express the complexity of the issue we are talking about. Looking at *Webster's Collegiate Dictionary*, for example, we find the following definitions: 'retardation: … slowness of development or progress'; 'handicap: … figuratively, any disadvantage that renders success more difficult'; 'disabled: … incapable; incapacitated.' It might come as a surprise that the most accepted term 'disabled' is actually the most limited and judgemental, opening no perspective, whereas 'handicapped' does not refer to the person herself but to the difficulties she has to cope with, thus describing the nature of the problem instead of labelling the person. Interestingly enough, the most disapproved term 'retarded' is, in its true sense, the most open-minded in terms of possible development and growth, as 'slow' in no way implies that development has stopped or is impossible. However, all these words might become disparaging when

---

1. Sinason, 1992.

used with a derogatory attitude. As long as people who are 'different' and who do not quite fit into what society considers 'normal' are met with disrespect and contempt, whatever name they are called will sooner or later be considered disparaging. If we keep in mind that to be handicapped, disabled, retarded, confused or demented etc., is not shameful, but a human condition, and that we have to accept and respect human beings suffering from these conditions, we are free again to use language appropriately and in a more differentiated way.

Therefore, as much as I am prepared to conform, wherever possible, with what is in common use, I shall now and then, where it is necessary to be more clear and explicit in what I have to say, take the liberty to use a term which might so far have been considered as 'not politically correct'. I do hope that for the readers the attitude of acceptance and esteem in which this is done will come through.

The male and female form for carers as well as for those they care for is used alternately.

2
Creating living spaces

Regardless of the difference in tasks of, for example, a nursing home, a community for people with special needs and an institution for adolescents with behaviour disorders, some fundamental considerations are applicable to any of the settings mentioned in this book.

Generally speaking, this book is about how to create living spaces for human beings who, for very different reasons, are not, not yet or not at all, in a position to live independently. Such spaces must offer conditions which meet the specific needs of the people concerned and support, as much as possible, their capacities, their independence and their taking responsibility for themselves. It is widely acknowledged that this is not just an issue of housing and feeding people, but a demanding and complex task which requires professional training and experience.

This certainly is an encouraging development, but there is also a 'dark side' to it. Together with the professional upgrading, ambitions grow. Carers define goals, try out methods and aim for changes, which sometimes correspond more to their own ambitions than to the needs of those they care for. Knowledge is useful, as it provides instruments to help other people to develop their abilities. But it may also result in a temptation to 'educate' other people. This is inappropriate with adults, and can be an arrogance which they usually refuse to accept.

Adults with special needs, even though their level of development may in some ways be comparable to that of a child, have lived lives too. Their years of experience cannot just be dismissed. Older people too, even though they may be weak, ill or disturbed, have lived their lives, the formative influence of which is still there. This we have to respect: even though their behaviour may appear bizarre, childish or unrealistic.

Adolescents are no longer children either, and they often refuse to be educated by others. And those considered to have 'challenging behaviour' usually have a long history of inadequate or failed education, which is unlikely to let them remain open for later catching up. Instead of trying to impose our educational ideas on them, we have to find other ways to facilitate their further growth, to encourage and support their taking responsibility for themselves.

It goes without saying that trying to 'educate' people in hospitals or nursing homes or communities for the elderly is totally inappropriate. But attempts to educate sneak in here too. Carers sometimes have a very precise idea about what is right for the people they take care of, and—with more or less energy—try to impose it on them.

To know about diagnostics is helpful, and sometimes even essential, to understand better the 'otherness' of others. But it could also inhibit a carer seeing the other person's abilities and entice him to look at reactions and behaviour exclusively from the viewpoint of symptomatology.

To be consciously aware of this 'dark side' makes it easier to avoid its dangers. This in no way implies that professional skills and knowledge are unnecessary, or that it is enough to rely on common sense and experience or to adopt an attitude of 'laissez-faire'. On the contrary, we need our knowledge to understand better the people we take care of, and we have to use our skills to support them in a way that meets their different personalities and needs. It makes a crucial difference if we view knowledge as a way of deepening our capacity to understand and enabling the other person to make her own decisions instead of using it as an irrefutable instrument to classify and determine other people.

What does it mean to work in a person-centred way?

It does *not* mean to look at a person isolated from the world around her and to attribute existing problems exclusively to the person herself. This is a widespread misunderstanding. There is a big temptation—or better, a danger—to do so with persons who suffer from mental disabilities or distress. They *are* difficult sometimes, there *are* problems with them—so it's easy to see *them* as the problem. This shouldn't be. There are many other factors influencing so-called 'challenging behaviour' to be considered when looking for reasons and solutions. The 'map of influencing factors'[1] might give some orientation. Sometimes, moving a bed or changing our own ways just a little is much more effective than the most cleverly devised educational measures—though, of course, it is not often that easy.

Working in a person-centred way means *not starting from ideas about how human beings should be, but from how they are and from their potential*. It means taking the other person seriously in her own individual way, attempting to understand her ways of expressing herself, and supporting her to find, within her limited possibilities, her own way to adequately cope with reality.

This attitude does not just apply to individuals. It is also helpful in dealing with a group, a team or a community. Working in a person-centred way means solving problems, developing programmes and taking decisions together *with* the people concerned, not *for* them. It means considering and respecting their different abilities, needs and opinions and, within their possibilities, allowing them to take responsibility for themselves. To work in a person-centred way means to be aware of, and to encourage, the resources of an organism—be this an individual or a community.

A person-centred attitude also applies to the carers themselves. They should learn to trust in their individual ways, their personal resources and abilities, and contribute them to their work. To work in a person-centred way means *to be transparent as a person*. This also requires that carers are willing to take into account their own part in a situation.

To work in this way also means to acknowledge clearly the frame of reference of a situation and of the people involved. On the one hand, there is the structure of the

---

1. see p. 6.

institution or community—its financial and organisational conditions, the responsibilities of the staff etc.—which has to be considered and made transparent for everybody involved. On the other hand, in some areas and situations, it may be necessary to create a structure that enables the other person to release resources and develop capabilities. How this structure has to be designed, in order not to restrict a person but to define a safe space for self-determination, will differ according to different fields, different tasks and individual circumstances. To recognise the appropriate structure, and offer it to the other person, is a crucial aspect of person-centred work.

The concept presented here is aimed at providing orientation for the carers and supporting them in terms of how to cope with the standards described above in their everyday work.

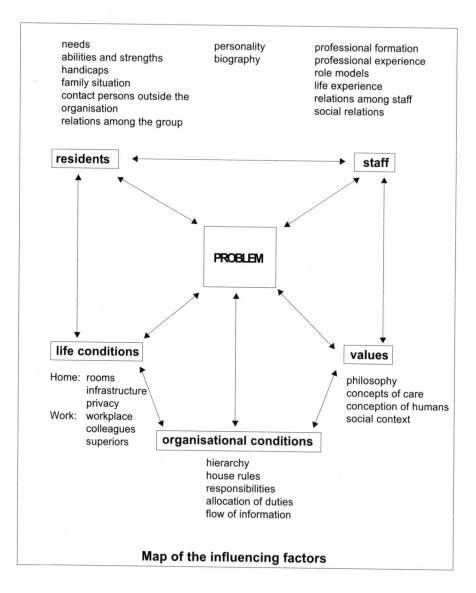

Map of the influencing factors

Why do we need a concept?

Is the professional training and competence of social workers, carers, nurses and teachers for special education not sufficient? Perhaps another concept—or concepts in general—inhibit spontaneous reactions and restrict individual ways of working? Surely a concept results in working mechanically along a rigid pattern, instead of being open to react to the particular situation?

If a concept has this effect, it is either not suitable or not properly applied. To work with a concept does not imply constantly staring at it and considering at each step if it does, or does not, conform. Most of the time we react spontaneously, and it cannot be the purpose of a concept to prevent spontaneity. But having a concept in the back of our minds extends the radius of our spontaneity and, at the same time, defines its frame. A concept represents a frame of reference which:

- defines the goals, fundamentals and priorities of our work
- acts as a guide and, at the same time, defines the open space for the staff's individual ways and initiatives
- offers a structure with which carers can compare their actions
- serves as a guideline when doubts arise or situations become critical
- offers criteria to compare differing opinions and clarify disagreements.

Moreover, a concept facilitates an effective staff policy. When hiring new carers, it allows us to:

- compare mutual expectations and ideas in a concrete way
- recognise differing opinions more quickly
- prevent wrong decisions and misunderstandings on both sides.

And it may, to some extent, prevent the people being cared for from being used as an experimental field for the staff to try out their different educational and philosophical ideas.

A concept grants continuity, not in the sense of dull routine, but of attitudes and conditions which also offers space for individual ways and is open to further development and necessary change. This kind of continuity can considerably improve the climate and the ways of living together in an institution or a community. Work will become less frustrating for the staff and more relaxed, as well as more interesting, if it is informed by a concept which, on the one hand, offers clear guidelines and, on the other, requires initiative, creativity and alert attention for the different personalities of those in care. They will feel better and more secure if they can rely on the continuity of some basic conditions.

The following two examples, both concerning adult women with special needs, will help to introduce the subject and illustrate the idea.

Example 1
Gertrud is constantly hurting herself by picking bits of skin off her hands. For years the staff of the institution she lives in have tried in vain to stop her doing

this. She rubs her bleeding hands on the walls, which are bloodstained wherever she goes. This absorbs her so much that she is hardly able to participate in the activities of the group. One day the staff decide to give up trying to stop her. Gertrud is now allowed to pick the skin off her hands, but under certain conditions: she has to decide if she wants to stay with the others and participate in their activities, or if she wants to pick her skin. If she decides to do that, she can do it on the sofa in the corner. If she wants to join the group activities at the big table, she has to stop it. The result is amazing: Gertrud still picks the skin off her hands, but considerably less now. The walls are not bloodstained any more. Her hands are less sore. In the morning, before the group activities start, she sometimes mumbles: 'Must decide, must decide,' and she always keeps the agreement not to pick the skin off her hands; as long as she participates in the activities of the group.

Example 2

Eva does not like housework. She complains violently whenever she has to do it. Everybody knows this and tries to calm her down. She continues to scream about the vacuum cleaner. One day, a staff member examines it more carefully and discovers that, indeed, there is a loose switch, which has to be held down with one finger in a very uncomfortable way. It is easy to get this switch fixed. And, in this way, the staff members are in a better position to deal with Eva's resistance to participating in the housework as it happens rather than interpreting a technical problem as 'resistance'.

At first, Gertrud and Eva were met with a 'diagnostic' and 'educational' attitude. The staff knew their deficiencies and, through experience and knowledge, considered themselves able to interpret the behaviour of the two women. In vain they tried to change the 'undesirable behaviour' which, on the contrary, increased and escalated into power fights with the staff. The successful solutions show a different attitude. The carers no longer worked from the assumption that they had a better understanding of what was right for the two women, but took them seriously and let them participate in the search for new ways. Instead of destructive power fights, constructive solutions were found with both of them.

Instead of trying to stop Gertrud's inappropriate behaviour, she was given space to make her own decisions, as well as a structure which helped her change her behaviour. Eva's protestations were no longer dismissed as her usual well-known reaction to something she did not like. The staff took it seriously and tried to find out what it really was about. And, as it turned out, Eva's perception had been quite realistic and there was a concrete reason for her complaining.

The two examples are different, and concern two quite different personalities. Gertrud showed a severely disturbed behaviour which not only strongly affected herself, but also the people around her. With Eva, it was a simple, everyday situation which had no big impact, but nevertheless caused unnecessary tension and bad feeling. Gertrud is a severely disabled woman who barely talks. She has lived for years in this institution, where she participates in a special day programme for those who are not able to work in a sheltered workshop. Eva, however, is only mildly disabled and well able to express herself verbally. She lives in a small flat-sharing community for people with special needs and works in a sheltered workshop.

A side effect, perhaps even more important than the resolution of the problem itself, was that the women's self-confidence had been reinforced, as they experienced themselves as being able to move and change things. And the staff learned that they could trust people with special needs much more than they had imagined.

To meet human beings—however disabled, 'difficult' or 'maladapted' they may be—with the conviction that *for them* their strange and unintelligible behaviour *makes sense*, and to try to understand it, is crucially different from just dismissing it as 'disturbed' and trying to control or stop it.

In both cases the attitude of the staff had positive effects. They intuitively discovered ways which corresponded to person-centred fundamentals, though they did not explicitly know about them. The next chapter will look at these 'fundamentals'.

3
Fundamentals of person-centred work

The person-centred approach has been developed by the American psychologist Carl Rogers (1902–1987), the founder of client-centred psychotherapy. At the beginning of his professional career, working with juveniles with behaviour disorders, Rogers found that his extensive theoretical knowledge did not help him much to really understand his clients. Adolescents and their parents frequently did not quite know what to do with his diagnosis and advice, however accurate it was. Rogers discovered that it was much more helpful to listen carefully to the other person, and he learned that changes were more likely to occur when he could grasp *the person's view* of what was going on. This insight motivated him to look for new ways in psychotherapy and to write his first book *Counseling and Psychotherapy,*[1] which received remarkable attention. From 1945 to 1957 at the University of Chicago Rogers had the opportunity to test, in practice, his ideas on psychotherapy as well as to teach them and to do research. Together with a group of motivated colleagues he founded the Chicago Counseling Center. In 1951 his standard work *Client-Centered Therapy*[2] was published. Very soon his thinking went beyond psychotherapy. He studied developmental aspects of the person[3] and, after moving to California in 1963 tried to apply his concepts to fields other than psychotherapy (groups, schools, companies, institutions). This extended application of his ideas he called the person-centred approach.[4]

The person-centred approach in other fields is based on the same fundamentals as client-centred therapy[5]. To understand what it means to work in a person-centred way in other fields it is vital to know these fundamentals. But it is equally indispensable to recognise clearly that, in other fields, they have to be realised in a different way than in psychotherapy. In the following, I shall first give a short summary of the basic theoretical fundamentals of the person-centred approach and then point to a few additional aspects that, in my view, are relevant when working with it. A basic essential is a humanistic image of human beings.

---

1. Rogers, 1942.
2. Rogers, 1951.
3. Rogers, 1961.
4. Rogers, 1969, 1970, 1977, 1980, 1982 .
5. These are described in detail in my book *Praxis der Gesprächspsychotherapie,* Pörtner (1994).

THEORETICAL FOUNDATIONS

A humanistic 'conception of man'

This philosophical approach views each human being as an autonomous and worthwhile person. It respects the differences of individuals. No two people are alike, not even two with the same disability or the same disease. Each individual has his own way of coping with life. A humanistic view starts from the assumption that every human being is basically working towards *growth* and *self-actualisation* and has his own personal resources to change and to solve problems. These resources may be disturbed or impaired for various reasons, including developmental disorders, traumatic experiences, lack of encouragement, diseases and old age. But they must be discovered and fostered. On principle *not we, but the person herself knows what is best for her,* although she may not have or have lost access to this knowledge.

Each person has to be taken seriously in her own personal way of expressing herself, even if we cannot immediately understand it. For that person it makes sense, and we have to respect that. We do not always succeed in decoding this 'sense'. We have to accept that often we cannot break through the wall and get to understand the inner world of persons with special needs, psychiatric patients or of confused elderly people. But to know that her behaviour *for her* makes sense, even though for us it remains concealed, implies an attitude which in itself has positive effects. To meet a person with the assumption that her behaviour for her has a meaning we do not understand makes us approach her differently than if we dismiss her as 'disturbed', 'crazy', or 'maladjusted'. We must try to '*feel into*' her perceptions and feelings even if they are not easily intelligible. Just *trying* to understand will change the quality of the relationship. Meeting people this way means tracking down hidden resources and awakening dormant potential, or at least helping to preserve and support existing abilities and thus prevent them from diminishing more and more. This attitude is one of the basic conditions of client-centred psychotherapy[6], and it is also a main condition for person-centred work in fields outside psychotherapy. But we always have to bear in mind the different context of different areas.

The three elements of the person-centred attitude

• *Empathy* is the ability to perceive sensitively and accurately the other person's experiencing and feelings; to enter her frame of reference as if we were the other person, but at the same time never to forget that we are ourselves and not the other. Empathy does not mean identification. Empathic understanding does not aim to interpret or classify the other person; rather it is an attempt to enter her world as accurately as possible. The experience of being understood in itself encourages growth.

---

6. Rogers, 1957.

• *Unconditional positive regard* means accepting the other person without judging her, just as she is at the moment, with all her difficulties and possibilities.

• *Congruence* means being consciously aware of our own experiencing and feelings, and being able to discriminate it from what we perceive in the other person. Congruence means meeting the client as the person we are, and not hiding behind a professional mask. This implies that we should be open to, and able to accept, our own feelings, impulses and impressions, but not to throw them unfiltered at the other person. We must be able to discern, within the frame of our task, when it makes sense to share our feelings and when it does not. Congruence also implies that the general set-up of a situation must be clear and transparent for all persons concerned.

The theory of self-concept[7] . . .

. . . allows a deeper understanding of what congruence means. It also helps to understand better the guidelines for person-centred work outlined in the next chapter.

The notion of self-concept embraces the image a person has of herself and how she values this image. The self-concept develops, on the one hand, out of the immediate experience of the child (for example, hunger-satisfaction) and, on the other hand, out of the values which are communicated to the child by the world around him (for example: 'If I get dirty, I am bad'). The self-concept is not fixed, but permanently developing and changing through the experiences a person has throughout her life.

Obstructions and emotional difficulties arise when experiences, feelings and sensations cannot be accepted, because they do not conform to the self-concept. In other words, the self-concept can be fixed by rigid external values or taboos (e.g. 'Getting angry is bad').

Congruence exists when *the self-concept conforms to experience*. The self-concept is flexible and able to accept and integrate new experience.

Incongruence exists when *a rigid self-concept* cannot allow new experiences, feelings or perceptions, unless they conform to the existing narrow limits. The others have to be denied, suppressed, rationalised, reinterpreted, or may not even be perceived.

As mentioned before, there are a few more crucial aspects to be considered in the practice of the person-cented approach. I shall specify, in particular, those which are relevant for the professional fields we are dealing with here.

PRACTICAL FOUNDATIONS

The balance between structure and freedom

It is very important to carefully acknowledge the structure of a situation. A carer has to be clearly aware of where her empathy is directed in this particular situation. She

7. Rogers, 1951.

should recognise where the boundaries are that she needs to respect, as well as where she herself has to define boundaries or to make demands. To neglect this frequently leads to misunderstandings and deceptions.

An everyday situation is different from a therapeutic situation. The frame of psychotherapy is the therapy session. Its central issue is the client's experiencing and the therapist's aiming to understand it as accurately as possible. The structure of a community is different. It requires that carers not only empathically understand those in their care, but also acknowledge the circumstances of the community. A simple example may illustrate this.

Example 3

John lives in a small flat-sharing community for people with special needs. He does not like to participate in the housework. Yet the people live in this community on condition that the house is basically kept by themselves. Every time John has to do the dishes, he complains vehemently, before finally doing them reluctantly and with much grumbling. How can the social worker in this situation be empathic and accepting? Not, of course, by doing the dishes herself, nor by getting somebody else do them, but by understanding and accepting John's anger and irritation, and by communicating this to him (for example: 'You are angry right now, because you have to do the dishes', 'You don't like to do the dishes.').

Thus John's feelings are empathically understood and his irritation accepted. But in terms of his duties the limits are clear; he has to do the dishes. This is a crucial distinction: on the one hand, the carer has to *empathically understand and accept the emotional reaction of the other person*, but, on the other hand, she has to *respect and represent the structure of the community*. Some carers have difficulty accepting structures and tend to blur them. However, many actions—especially those of adolescents—are aimed precisely at getting the boundaries clearly set, which silently are there anyway.

The boundaries are defined, on the one hand, by the structure of the community and by the specific circumstances of the particular situation, and, on the other hand, by the resources and limitations of the staff, and the resources and limitations of the clients. It is crucial to acknowledge and to take into consideration these boundaries, because only in this way can we recognise the space within which the person-centred attitude can work.

The balance between structure and freedom is a crucial factor in this work. It is relevant at various levels and in different contexts. Both structure *and* freedom are needed: they are interdependent, complementary and have to be maintained in a balance appropriate for the situation and for the people concerned. To keep on finding and maintaining this balance is an essential task for professionals in this field—be it working with people with special needs, or people in need of care or showing behavioural disorders. To offer the best possible conditions to live and develop always involves giving *as much structure as needed and as much freedom as possible*. Quite often only one is acknowledged and the other neglected.

In earlier years—and this still has some influence today—special education for people with special needs emphasised structure. It is true that structure is necessary. Yet if structure does not, at the same time, include space for a person's own decisions and initiatives, it will inhibit, more than promote, her growth. However, it does not help a person with special needs if we just aim at giving her freedom to make decisions, without attention to a helpful structure. If the space is not protected by defined boundaries, if it is too wide and open for her to survey, she will become stressed and unable to use it. It needs a structure to make the space visible. It needs leeway to make sure that the structure does not just restrict people, but defines a safe place where they are encouraged to try out their own impulses and make their own decisions.

Example 4

Hanna collects everything. Her room is stuffed with dolls, knick-knacks, old papers, empty boxes, etc.; she cannot throw anything away. Once in a while, when her room brims over, the social worker has a hard time trying to persuade Hanna that it needs to be tidied up. She does not want to sort out anything that she has accumulated. The social worker is reluctant to simply tell Hanna what she has to do, or to tidy up the room himself. He would like to leave it to Hanna. But when he tells her that, some time, she will have to tidy up her room, nothing happens. He has an idea: he sets a time limit within which the room has to be tidied up. Hanna can choose if she wants to do it by herself or with the social worker helping. It is also (within the set time limit) up to her when she will do it. As she is not able to give an immediate answer, he writes the different options on a sheet which he sticks to the wall and asks Hanna to mark her choice with an X. When the carer comes in the next day, Hanna has marked, 'Wednesday; together with social worker'.

This is a simple example of what it means to find an adequate balance between structure and freedom. Out of consideration for the room-mates as well as for hygiene reasons, Hanna cannot be excused from tidying her room. She *has to do it*—this is the structure. But within that structure Hanna has *a choice between different options*—this is the freedom.

Such minimal choices may seem unimportant to outsiders. For Hanna—and not only for her, but for anybody whose life is largely determined by others—any space for her own decisions is significant, however small it might be. To have options has an influence on life quality. To be allowed to make decisions means to be taken seriously and treated as an adult person, it means acting independently—even though in a limited area. Human beings for whom everything is decided by others, and who have no choices at all, will become either rebellious or apathetic. The former results in weary power fights, the latter in resignation. Certainly, neither way is beneficial, either for the person herself or for those around her. Therefore, her own decisions have not only to be respected, but stimulated and encouraged as much as possible.

To find an adequate balance between structure and freedom is a demanding task. It is not something static which can be discovered 'by diagnostics' and then fixed. It is a subtle balance, continuously to be watched and, if necessary, modified—not *for* the other person, but *together with* her. Carers must be attentively aware of changes and steps of growth. They have to carefully notice if and how the freedom is used, if it is too small or too large, and if, perhaps, the boundaries need to be altered.

Example 5

Herman cannot deal with his money. Every time he gets his salary at the workshop, he immediately spends it, to the last penny, at the shopping centre across the street. He has already accumulated hundreds of toy cars, and he continues to buy new ones. He then has no money left for other things. If, for instance, the group goes out for a coffee, one of them always has to pay for Herman. All attempts to persuade Herman that he should save money for such occasions and not spend it all on toy cars have failed. The very day Herman gets his salary, he compulsively spends it on toy cars. The social worker agrees with Herman to split the money into different envelopes, one for each week, and to take just one at a time, on the day indicated on the envelope. It works. Herman even seems to appreciate this support, and he keeps the agreement. Yet it is important for Herman to know that, on the day of payment when he comes home, the social worker will be there and, together with him, prepare the envelopes.

In this example, a narrower structure was helpful for Herman, as he could not handle the complete freedom to budget his money himself. He even felt relieved to get this support. Yet he still had some independence, because nobody controlled when he would take the envelopes with the money from the drawer. It remained his own responsibility to keep to the agreement.

Sensitivity to recognise individual possibilities and limitations, as well as openness for changes and flexibility to react to them, are required. But, equally important, is clarity about what is fixed and therefore cannot be negotiated.

Clarity . . .

. . . is something which may not naturally be connected with the person-centred approach, and indeed is often neglected. However, clarity is an indispensable condition for the person-centred attitude to work. Lack of clarity leads to the misconception that empathic understanding and acceptance are just a vague 'being nice' and 'laissez-faire' attitude. Staff, wishing to be democratic, frequently tend not to acknowledge facts—especially unpleasant ones—or to blur them, even for themselves. Thus they ignore the need for congruence, which for the person-centred attitude is at least as important as the two other elements. Congruence also implies clarity about the boundaries within which decisions are possible, and about facts that cannot be changed.

Many people working in social professions have a hard time providing this clarity. They tend to discuss everything, even matters on which the other person finally has no influence at all. Yet there is nothing more disappointing than the illusion of having a choice when there is none. Certainly staff members do not always deliberately create such illusions. Often, only after discussing it with the other person, do they realise that, in fact, the decision has already been made.

Example 6

A small community for people with special needs is to admit a new member. Two people have applied. Both are invited for a visit. Afterwards the staff discusses with the group whom they would choose. The group expresses a clear preference. Only later staff and management realise that, for reasons the residents could neither know nor judge, this young man cannot be accepted and they decide on the other applicant. It is quite understandable that the residents are irritated and complain about their choice not having been acknowledged and about the staff first asking them, but then still making the decision over their heads.

Management and staff definitely should have verified whether there was a real choice for the group, before discussing it with them. It would have spared these people with special needs another experience of being disappointed and not taken seriously. Such experiences do not reinforce trust, but leave people feeling discouraged. A little more reflection could help to avoid that.

Confusion, arising from thoughtlessness, does not just happen for people with special needs. I remember an example from a regular primary school.

Example 7

In a second grade class a new teacher is to temporarily replace the current teacher who will be on leave for six months. Several applying teachers give test lessons. After that, the regular teacher discusses with the class the different applicants; whom they liked more and whom less. The children take this very seriously, as they believe that their opinion will be taken into consideration for the selection. The teacher who is finally hired is the one they liked the least.

It is easy to figure out the dreadful effect this had on the children's trust in adults. And it was not helpful for the new teacher either. He had a very difficult start, and failure was predictable. The general situation—that the new teacher was to be selected by a board, on which neither the current teacher nor the opinion of the children had any influence—had neither been taken into account, nor made transparent. Discussing the matter with the children simply raised futile expectations, which afterwards were disappointed. A sensible way to let the children participate would have been to tell them which teacher had been selected, and then to discuss their reactions, feelings and worries.

Carers are sometimes reluctant to give their clients clear information about something which has already been decided. They ask for their opinion, as if it could still have an influence, and at the same time try to make the taken decision sound appealing to them. In other words, they try to manipulate those they are caring for towards where they want them to go. People with special needs are relatively easy to manipulate. To avoid this is another reason why clarity is necessary. Fairness requires informing people clearly about given facts, and then accepting that the other person may not be pleased. Here again, we need to be empathic and take the experience of the other person seriously. We have to acknowledge and accept her feeling of disappointment, anger, irritation or sadness.

Experience as an essential factor

How something is experienced is at least as important, and sometimes much more so, than *what* has happened. Each person's experience is different. What may terribly upset or scare one person does not bother the other. What somebody may experience as intrusive may be helpful for somebody else. What for one person is a pleasure, is a burden for the other. Experience is subjective.

The subjective experience is a central aspect of the personality; a key for understanding and an access to resources. This still is not sufficiently taken into account. We tend to take our knowledge, our norms (and sometimes also our own subjective experience!) as an objective standard—although the other person cannot relate to it, because it does not conform to the way she is experiencing. A carer tries to persuade a woman with a disability that the situation is actually different from what she feels, instead of trying to understand how she experiences it, and to go from there. A nurse tells a patient what he has to do in order to feel better, instead of being interested in how he experiences and deals with his disease, and in the resources he could mobilise. Changes can only occur from a person's own experiencing, not from outside. To feel that her experiences are understood can be of vital help for a person's ability to change. Therefore it is essential that carers are able to be empathic with the people they have to take care of.

Example 8

Roland, a man in his eighties, has recently been moved to a nursing home. He is very confused and quite rebellious. He is incontinent and no longer able to wash himself. But he fiercely refuses to be washed by the nurse and turns away from her, so that she cannot reach him. The nurse tries to persuade him to turn around, but this only makes things worse. The more the nurse tries, the more violently Roland defends himself. The nurse gets more and more impatient, but then all at once she realises that an impasse has been reached. She relaxes for a second, takes a deep breath and tries to imagine how Roland might feel. Then she says: 'You feel embarrassed, Roland, because I have to wash you, which is why you turn away from me.' Roland turns around and docilely allows the nurse to wash him.

The example shows how helpful it can be, for both sides, when carers in difficult situations try to understand what their client is experiencing. It is not without reason that experience has such an important place in humanistic psychology. Recent approaches in nursing based on humanistic fundamentals (see Chapter 11) also view the subjective experience of the patient as an important factor that should be paid more attention to. Even in medicine the importance of subjective experience is increasingly acknowledged.

Change lies in personal resources, not deficiencies

Sometimes the limitations of a person are so much the focus of attention that what is there is hardly noticed. Thus, abilities cannot grow, but will wither. Yet the potential for development and change does not lie in the deficiencies, but in the resources. These have to be discovered, encouraged and made use of. The 'diagnostic eye' which constantly looks at deficiencies tends to focus on what people with special needs— or the elderly, or the ill, or the maladapted—cannot do, blurring the view of what they still can do.

Older people tend to judge themselves—and to be judged—mainly by what they are no longer able to do, or what has become worse. Thus, new aspects that could emerge are overlooked. For example, confused older people whose thinking is impaired, sometimes develop new emotional and intuitive qualities.

Of course, we must not turn a blind eye to a person's limitations. But it is essential to realise that limitations can be considered from different viewpoints. Looking at limitations from the viewpoint of what is actually there is quite different from looking at them and seeing something missing. To start from what is there, implies that there is some potential for growth, and that perhaps the boundaries could be moved a little bit.

Example 9
John has to prepare a carrot salad. He bought two pounds of carrots and asks the social worker, 'Do I have to prepare them all?' The social worker shows him the other salads, already prepared, and asks him to guess how many carrots might be needed. 'I can't do that' is John's clear statement. The social worker is disappointed that John seems unable to make any progress on that score.

This could be seen differently: I think it *is* a progress that John is so clearly aware of his limitations and asks for help. It shows that he copes with this problem in a realistic way. Instead of just noting John's lack of imagination, the carer should also pay attention to and encourage what *is* there: John's being realistic about his ability and knowing when he needs help. This is a resource which could be further developed and of use in other situations too. This example also demonstrates that very small steps sometimes bear the potential for further development.

Small steps . . .

. . . that are so easily overlooked are particularly meaningful. Each step, as small as it may be, proves that a person is able to move forward, and carries the potential for further steps. Therefore, carers should meticulously look for these small steps—with a magnifying glass so to speak—and welcome them wherever they detect them.

Steps of growth can only be integrated if a person is allowed to take them *at her own pace*. This is particularly true for people with special needs. In a life widely determined by the pace of 'normal' people, they permanently experience being overtaken and falling behind. Some of them, especially the mildly disabled, develop considerable skills to hide this. The carers sometimes do not even notice it and this causes further stress. The experience of being inadequate and unable to follow is so omnipresent and overwhelming for most people with special needs that they hardly notice the small steps they *do* achieve here and there.

This is not only true for those with special needs. A great many people are much more clearly aware of what they did not (or not yet) achieve, than of the things they did achieve, and therefore feel depressed and hopeless. It is worth concentrating our focus on these small steps. Each step gives rise to hope and courage even if it leads— as we could see in the previous example—in a different direction from the one the carers had expected.

The road is as important as the destination

The crux in defining so-called educational or behavioural goals for a person with special needs is that success is defined in terms of achieving the goal. Eyes are so fixed on the goal that what happens on the way is overlooked. Impulses pointing in another direction are not attended to, although they might open up new perspectives; if only the carers would not stick so closely to their defined goal. For a person with special needs, the experience of being on the road, able to move and change something, is sometimes much more important than arriving at a specific destination or solving a particular problem. The person no longer experiences herself as blocked, but as being on the move. This must be noticed and encouraged by the staff.

Example 10
In an adult continuing education programme, people with special needs learn how to express their concerns. Paul has always wished to have a single room, but never dared to say so. In a role-play, he has the opportunity to demonstrate how he could express his concern to those in charge in his institution. The next evening at the programme, he happily tells the group, 'Have said it' and 'Lottery'. As this institution provides only a limited number of single rooms, and several people are applying, the staff has decided to do a lottery the next time a single room is available. And Paul is lucky: he wins the single room ticket. This happens just before the summer break. After that a new programme starts, in which again Paul participates. The facilitator asks him how he is doing in his single room. Paul says, 'No single room anymore. Much too boring.'

In this case priority had not been given to the goal, but to the road Paul covered. His wishes had been taken seriously. He was allowed to make his own experiences, and afterwards to change his mind. Although the staff felt they could have told Paul in advance that he would not like the single room, they let him, step by step, experience this process himself, and accepted what he decided upon. It is quite obvious that such an experience is much more rewarding for a person than a decision made by others 'for his own good'.

This *process-oriented view* which acknowledges and accepts changes, rather than sticking to what was known before, is characteristic of person-centred work, which aims to encourage personal growth.

Trusting the potential for growth

This, at first sight, may seem to be a strange principle, only justified perhaps when working with adolescents, where the task actually is to foster growth. But isn't this trust out of place in the group of people we are dealing with here? Is growth still possible at all with older, or even confused, people in need of care? Did not their development stop, or is it even declining? Should ill persons not just recover or, if this is not possible any more, *accept* their disease? What has this to do with growth? And, being a person with special needs, does this not imply that at some point no more growth is possible? Isn't it the carers' task, at this point, to help out and give support? How should they trust the potential of growth?

As long as they live, human beings have again and again to confront and cope with changing circumstances. Restrictions also represent changes and require a different perspective. Changes may concern, for example, the environment, a new carer, a different room, a new room-mate ; or the person herself, her aches and pains, losing her sense of orientation etc. A disease, too, may imply new perception and growth, as it requires modifications of self-image, attitudes or way of life, in order to cope with and feel as comfortable as possible in the new situation.

Often lifetime habits no longer conform to changed circumstances. They have to be given up and new ones found. This also means growth. In this way, even with older, confused people, or those with a disability, there is still growth, as, within the realm of their possibilities, they have to cope with new situations. If we start from the assumption that an organism basically is aimed at realising resources to optimally adapt to new circumstances, it does not seem too much out of place to trust the potential for growth and to encourage it as much as possible.

With adolescents it goes without saying that we have to trust their potential to develop. However, those who are considered neglected or who are frequently displaying behaviour problems are given alarmingly poor opportunities. Much too often it is by restricting measures that carers try to stop undesired behaviour and to enforce specific changes, whereas they should provide an adequate structure and enough freedom for the young person to take her own steps of development.

Are adults with special needs in any position to modify the rigid behaviour patterns marked in their childhood? Are older people still able to let go of cherished habits and principles, and develop new ways? It seems realistic not to expect too much, but to remain open to surprises. It is sometimes amazing the unexpected steps a person suddenly takes, which nobody would have believed them capable of.

Example 11

Bernard, a 37-year old man with severely impaired hearing, not able to talk and with strongly autistic features, when having a meal with his family, as soon as he had finished eating, used to get up and settle down in his favourite chair in the other room, whilst the others still sat together and talked. Only recently, for the first time, he came back after a while and sat with the others at the table until everybody got up. And also, not long ago, he who all his life had avoided touching, for the first time laid his hand upon his mother's hand and left it there for a while. His family remained speechless; all at once Bernard was showing behaviours they had never seen before. Obviously Bernard is not just stuck in his emotional development.

A person-centred attitude implies basically trusting in a person's potential to grow, but—and this is equally essential—does not *force* growth. *Only when a person is accepted just as she is does change become possible.* But a time of stasis may also make sense and be a necessary breather to enable a person to take the next step.

If no further development is possible, it is important for the carers *not to reinforce rigid patterns or reduce even more the limited opportunity for growth.* Frequently, carers underestimate, or do not see, this demanding aspect which not only requires an attitude that does not ignore the potential for growth, but also does not force change.

Personal responsibility

The person-centred approach highly values personal responsibility. It believes that each and every person, regardless of their abilities, is capable of taking some responsibility for themselves.

Personal responsibility is not an absolute notion. We cannot concede personal responsibility to a newborn baby. Learning to take more and more responsibility in ever larger areas is an essential aspect of growing. To respect and encourage, as much as possible, the client's personal responsibility is a basic concern in person-centred work.

People in need of care have, of course, only limited opportunities to take responsibility. Unfortunately this frequently results in taking all of them away. Yet there is always an area, as tiny and insignificant as it may appear, in which they *can* take personal responsibility. And in this area it *has* to be fostered. Carers, instead of thinking 'I know better' should discover such areas and encourage those they care for to take responsibility. For a severely disabled person, this could mean letting her decide herself if she wants the door open or closed. Or for another person, letting her choose if she wants to take the umbrella or get wet when going outside—something seemingly quite basic may represent an opportunity for people to take responsibility for themselves. Why is this so important?

Taking responsibility implies being taken seriously and not being totally dependent on others. This has an influence on life quality and self-esteem. The more restricted the opportunities for a person taking responsibility for herself, the more important it is not to take them away from her *completely*. Otherwise her ability to do so will deteriorate more and more and her dependence on others increase.

Example 12

After a stroke, Lore is paralysed and no longer able to speak. She lives in a nursing home. A friend is visiting who relates to her very sensitively, and whose presence Lore obviously enjoys. A nurse comes in to clear away the coffee tray. Suddenly he remembers that a children's choir is giving a performance in the lobby for the residents of the nursing home. He takes the wheelchair, saying, 'Let's go, Lore, we have a performance out there!' and drives the flabbergasted Lore out of the room, without noticing the equally flabbergasted visitor, nor confirming whether Lore is at all interested in the choir, or would prefer to stay in her room with her friend.

Unfortunately, very often, everyday life in institutions is determined by such ways of not acknowledging the residents' personal responsibilities. The nurse certainly meant well, as he did not want Lore to miss the special event. But 'meaning well' does not give anybody the right to ignore the desires and personal responsibilities of people in need of care. This approach results in progressively increasing their dependence until they are no longer able to make a decision and take responsibility for it.

From the foundations described above, we can deduce some useful guidelines for everyday living and working.

Signpost 1   Practical foundations

The balance between structure and freedom
Clarity
Experience as an essential factor
Change lies in personal resources, not deficiencies
Small steps
The road is as important as the destination
Trusting the personal growth
Personal responsibility

4

Guidelines for everyday work

These guidelines offer an explanation of what is essential in person-centred work and what it emphasises in practice. It is not a matter of rigid regulation but of a structure that gives orientation. We have always to ask: *what do the guidelines mean in this concrete situation, with this person, under these circumstances.*

The basic condition for carers is to be genuinely interested in the people they have to take care of. *Without genuine interest in other human beings and in how each person is different and has her own idiosyncratic ways, these guidelines could not be practised in a meaningful way, but would remain just empty phrases.*

Listening . . .

. . . is *the basic* foundation of person-centred work: listening to a handicapped person who has difficulties expressing herself; listening to older people even if what they say sounds unrealistic and confused; listening to adolescents, however immature and weird their ideas may appear; listening for nuances, for clues of change, own impulses, needs or desires, for feelings and moods. Listening is essential to understanding how another person feels and what she needs, but also for the carer to find out how to respond to her. Without listening there is no satisfying care-taking or support. Carers have to listen before they can do anything or make necessary arrangements for the other person. And it means *to listen with all senses,* to reactions, feelings and sensations which are not verbally expressed.

This also means *looking*—not in the sense of 'observing the behaviour' of the other person in order to interpret and judge her, but in the sense of *entering her world and carefully paying attention to clues of her experiencing.* Does somebody appear tense or relaxed, does he look scared, or sad, or happy? Does she tend to come close, or does she prefer to withdraw? How does he react to what I do, what does he seem to like and to dislike?

Taking the other person seriously

Even if a person expresses herself in an unintelligible way and her behaviour appears bizarre, she should always be taken seriously. A nurse should take it seriously when a patient complains about pain, even if she thinks she knows from experience that such severe pains are impossible in this case, or that the pain relief she gave the patient must have had its effects long since. The carer should take seriously what the old woman is saying, even when she finds it hard to believe.

Example 13

Alice, a woman of eighty-two, lives in a nursing home. In talking with a Spanish-speaking employee, she recalls a trip to Argentina she had made when she was eighteen. She tells the nurse about the ocean-liner on which she had travelled, and about her uncle's estate where she had stayed. For the nurse this is an unknown world in which she does not believe. As Alice is confused sometimes, the nurse dismisses her account as pure fantasy. She is only half-listening, saying 'mm' from time to time. Alice is aware of it and gets upset. By chance, Alice's daughter comes by. She knows about this trip to Argentina, which actually had represented a major event in her mother's life. The nurse is quite surprised and has a hard time accepting this, because it does not fit the idea of this confused old woman she had formed in her mind.

So the event Alice clearly remembered—despite her temporary confusion—had been absolutely real and meaningful for her life. To listen carefully to her and take her story seriously would have given the nurse useful insights into Alice's former life and the world she had lived in and could have opened new perspectives in how to respond to her.

However, usually it does not even matter if the facts are true or not. What is important is that for the other person it has meaning at that moment. *This* must be taken seriously. Perhaps it is just an image for a mood, a feeling, a desire or for whatever she may have in mind and cannot express differently. This showed also in the course of psychotherapy with the mentally disabled 20-year-old Catherine[1].

Example 14

Catherine, in nearly every session, fantasised about accidents and hospitals; she had to go to the hospital this morning and the ambulance came to pick her up, or the hospital had called, she should come and hold somebody's hand during his operation, etc. Though this was obviously not true, I took it seriously and responded to what she told me. After a while it turned out that these hospital fantasies were reminiscences of a traumatic experience she so far had never been able to process; at 15 she had been sterilised, without anybody preparing her for the operation or explaining to her what she would have to go through.

These examples make it very clear how essential it is to take seriously what a person tries to express, and not to dismiss it as a 'handicapped' or 'confused' person talking, even if we cannot understand or believe it. To try to *'feel into' her subjective perception and frame of reference* not only causes a person to feel better understood, it will also

---

1. Pörtner, 1990.

open new horizons of understanding for the carers, thus making their work more interesting and more alive.

Needs and desires, too, must be taken seriously, regardless of whether they can be met. Whether a desire is accepted, even though for some reason it cannot be fulfilled, or dismissed as improper, feels quite different. The example of little Cathy (described in Chapter 10) very nicely illustrates this difference. However, we often have a hard time with this differentiation. We tend to identify accepting with granting, and to dismiss a desire or a need if we are not able to grant it. Could this also have something to do with our difficulty of accepting our own limits—in this case of not being able to meet the other person's needs?

To take a person seriously implies another principle which should go without saying, but actually is very often neglected: in the presence of a person with special needs *never talk about her, but always with her.* To talk about people as if they were not there, although they are present in the same room, is a bad habit quite common in institutions as well as in families. People do this not only with children, but also with adults, especially with the disabled or confused, thinking: 'They do not understand it anyway.' This is an error. People who cannot hear or are not able to express themselves verbally, are usually very sensitively aware of others talking about them and of the mood in which it is done. The negative effect of this repeated experience of 'not being there' on self-esteem and a person's contact with reality is obvious.

Comparing with 'normality'

Considering that which is 'normal' with a person in our care, even though she is disabled, confused or mentally ill, reinforces her reality contact. This, of course, does not mean overstressing them with demands that do not take account of their handicaps. Yet we should not qualify every 'difficult' behaviour as a 'special need', but ask ourselves if it could not just represent a personal peculiarity we would easily tolerate in a 'normal' person.

Example 15
Otto lives in a flat-sharing community for adults with special needs. The inhabitants take it in turns to do the housekeeping and prepare the meals. Otto is not able to make a salad dressing. The staff repeatedly try to demonstrate and explain to him how to do it. But he does not get it and always takes the bottle with the ready-made dressing. The staff are disappointed that he is unable to learn such a simple thing.

A learning disability may well be the reason why Otto is not able to understand how to prepare a salad dressing. On the other hand, many 'normal' people think they cannot make a good dressing and prefer the ready-made variety, without therefore being regarded as disabled. We could also see it this way: Otto estimates realistically his ability to make a salad dressing, and taking the 'ready made' bottle is an adequate way of dealing with the situation.

In the example of Alice and her trip to Argentina, we have seen how quickly carers sometimes dismiss an older person's quite realistic statement as confused, as soon as it does not conform to what they are used to. With psychiatric patients there is also the danger of seeing any unusual way of behaviour as a symptom.

Example 16

Helga, after a suicide attempt, is admitted to a psychiatric hospital. After getting over the acute crisis, she wants to hire, at her own expense, a private teacher to give her Arabic lessons during her stay—something the structure of this private clinic would certainly allow. However, the ward staff regards this as weird, as an example of her loss of reality contact, even as a psychotic symptom. The patient's desire is not met. Instead, she is told to participate in the activities the ward provides to reinforce the patient's reality contact. What doctors and nurses do not know (and what they easily could have learned by talking with her) is that Helga is planning to start a degree in Romance languages, and Arabic is, if not an essential, a very useful foundation for a deeper understanding of Romance languages. From this aspect, Helga's desire was not weird at all.

Within the *context of her life,* Helga's wish to take Arabic lessons had more reality contact than the activities the ward provides. This had not been acknowledged and thus a chance to support *the patient's contact with the reality of her own life* had been missed.

Of course, it is impossible for carers to know everything about the life context of their clients. But that's exactly why they should not treat as a symptom anything they do not understand. For the time being they should work with the situation as they find it and take the other person's concern seriously. The shortest way to find out, within the context of her life, whether this concern is realistic, is to empathically respond to her. This implies that carers should stay only with the obvious: the statements, behaviours and experiences of those in their care as they manifest themselves at that particular moment.

Staying with the obvious

We should avoid interpretations and explanations based on a person's disability or disorder. We should not deny, depreciate or reinterpret, thinking we know better, but first of all stay with the obvious, *exactly with what the other person tries to express*.

Example 17

A patient with a not yet well-known syndrome is admitted to a hospital for several weeks of treatment. For many years he has studied everything he could get hold of about his disease, which is chronic and quite painful. However, for the staff his illness is relatively new. The patient has clear ideas about how he wishes to be treated. He brings along books and computer printouts concerning his treatment. This gets on the nerves of the nurses. They complain that the patient is difficult, always wanting something else and ringing for the nurses ten times a day. The consultant first encourages them to fully express their annoyance, then he asks: 'How does the patient experience his disease, how has he integrated it into his everyday life?' The staff has no idea. Now one of the nurses is told to ask the patient about these issues and then inform the others. The conversation with the patient opens completely new perspectives. All at once the person behind the 'case' emerges and is taken seriously. This enables the team to organise the nursing services in a way that suits and helps the patient better, and is, at the same time, much more satisfying for themselves.

This detour could have been avoided had the staff stayed with the obvious. The patient, with his books and treatment diagrams, signalled, 'I know a lot about my disease and would like to have a say in my treatment'. Taking this concern seriously would have shown interest and responding to it would have led very quickly to important questions for the planning of the treatment. How does the patient experience his disease, how does he deal with it, and what are his resources?

Example 2 (p. 8) with Eva and the vacuum cleaner showed how important it is, in living with people with special needs, to stay with the obvious. With a 'normal' person it would go without saying that we first check if something is wrong with the vacuum cleaner before we assume that something is wrong with the person. It should be the same with somebody with special needs. Only when the obvious does not make any sense should we try to find out what the hidden meaning could be. And the best way to approach this is to stay accurately and concretely with what the person is expressing and, together with her, go with it step by step. In this context there is another important principle.

Don't let your guide be what you already know

Carers should not think that they know how a person will react, even if they have seen it happen a hundred times. It is possible, at any time, that a person will act completely differently. We should be open to that and not stick to what we already know about a person. This was clearly shown in Example 11, (p.21)of Bernard. Of course, in many situations, our knowledge about a person's history and way of life may be very useful (see Example 32, p.39). But carers should not use it to restrict themselves—and the person they take care of—but *should always stay open to new and unknown aspects of her personality.*

Facilitating and responding to a person's experiencing

A person's subjective way of experiencing must be taken into account if we want to create adequate conditions for her well-being. Only by paying attention to how a person is experiencing are carers able to proceed in a sensible way. Does the older man in the nursing home appreciate it when the radio is turned on, or does he look annoyed? How is it for Laura to be washed by a male nurse? Does Dora like it when the carer passes her hand over her hair, or does she find it intrusive? Is Frank pleased when the nurse puts his wheelchair to the table where the others are sitting, or would he prefer to stay by himself and look out the window? Does Alice enjoy the sun shining on her bed, or is the bright light too strong for her eyes? Carers must be able to respond to these things. Wherever possible, they should try to diminish what is experienced as unpleasant, and to develop what feels agreeable.

It is not always possible to change an environment or situation to the way a person wishes, but at least it gives her relief to be able to express desires and worries and to be taken seriously by the carers.

Example 18

A visitor wants to take Dora for a walk. She finds Dora crying at the entrance of the nursing home. It turns out that Dora is scared when the others have an argument. She would like to run away and vanish. After that the nurses pay more attention to Dora as soon as it becomes loud on the ward. They talk with her or take her aside. This way Dora feels less panicked.

Sometimes it is possible, without much effort, to change something that is experienced as bad, threatening, frightening or just unpleasant; this may be something very ordinary.

Example 19

Seventeen-year-old Oscar recently joined the community for juveniles with behaviour disorders. He refuses to take a shower. The social workers try to convince him, to force him—it is hopeless. He shirks whenever he can. It is a weary, escalating fight. Finally, the consultant has an idea: the social workers should propose that Oscar takes a bath. That's what they do: they even offer him a bubble bath. Oscar is delighted, and from that moment his personal hygiene is not a problem anymore.

There is no objective reason why taking a shower should be unpleasant and taking a bath pleasant, it is just Oscar's subjective feeling. By taking that into account and allowing him a bath from time to time, instead of forcing him to take a shower, the staff and Oscar have been spared many a fruitless argument and this has considerably contributed to the good relations between them.

As much as possible human beings should be allowed *to make their own experiences*. This again not only, but particularly, applies to people with special needs. Very simple everyday things which frequently, without much thinking, are done for the other person spoil their chances of making an experience and learning from it. It is much more helpful, for example, to take somebody outside for a minute and let her experience for herself whether she would be too warm with the coat or too cold without it, than to just say: 'Today you need your warm coat'. The same is actually true with children.

Of course there are limits. There are situations where people with special needs have to be protected from bad experiences. But this is something which is over-emphasised rather than neglected. To protect a person from any bad experience also means preventing her from learning to confront her reality and making her miss chances for good experiences. It is very important, though, not to leave somebody alone with a bad experience, but to talk it over with him and to consider together what could be learned from it.

To be aware of how a person experiences may also help to better understand so called 'undesired behaviours' and to eventually develop alternatives.

Example 20

Bernard—whom we met in Example 11—for some time now, before going to bed in the evening, holds his hands endlessly under the running water. The carers have a hard time persuading him to stop it and turn the water off. He never does it by himself. Perhaps the carers should try to find out what meaning this behaviour might have for Bernard. Perhaps it is a pleasant sensation to feel the running water on his hands? Perhaps they could try to give him a bowl filled with water where he could play with his hands. Or perhaps an hourglass could help to limit his habit to an acceptable scale.

These are just two of many possible ideas for how to deal with this behaviour. Perhaps none will work and the carers will have to think again and try something completely different. Yet trying to understand and possibly change behaviour by taking into account the other person's experiencing, is in any case much more useful than making a fight out of it—which most of the time will be useless anyway. Even if it is not possible to obtain major change, trying to grasp the behaviour of the other person through her way of experiencing helps to understand her better. Last, but not least, this way of proceeding is considerably more interesting and rewarding for the carers than the weary attempts at stopping undesired behaviour or persuading the other person that things are different from how she experiences them.

Example 21

Elvira and Fanny live in a home for elderly people. They like each other and often spend time together. One day Fanny loses her key. Elvira is terribly upset and feels guilty about this happening to her friend. Although she had not been there when it happened, she cannot calm down and repeats constantly, 'It's my fault that Elvira lost her key.' The carer tries to talk her out of that, but in vain. Elvira repeats it over and over again. Finally the carer tries it in a different way: 'You are sad because Fanny lost her key, right Elvira?'. Elvira nods and very soon calms down.

Instead of persisting with her attempts to persuade Elvira, the carer tried to understand what was going on in her mind. Elvira obviously felt understood and could now let go of her self-accusation. This is one of many examples showing that it is much more helpful to respond to another person's *experience* than to argue about facts. Older people, having moved to an institution, frequently say, 'I want to go home', and the usual answer is, 'Your home is here now'. Very often they then get upset and protest. A wearing discussion takes place, until one of the parties finally gives up. It would make much more sense to try to grasp the experience expressed in their words: 'You are homesick', or 'You often think of home', or 'You are not quite settled in here yet'.

Encouragement

In the course of their lives, people with special needs are discouraged over and over again. There are so many things they would like to, but cannot do. They either lose confidence in themselves or overestimate their capabilities and get discouraged once more. Older people are often discouraged by the diminishing of their abilities and lose confidence even in what they *are* still able to do.

Of course, we cannot meet these feelings with platitudes such as, 'It is not as bad as all that.' But carers should pay careful attention to any sign of hope or courage and support it. They should reinforce a person when she achieves something, however insignificant it may appear. Small steps should not perish in the daily routine, but must be noticed and encouraged.

This is equally true for adolescents who are considered as having behaviour disorders. Very rarely, in the course of their lives, have they been encouraged, but over and over again confronted with their failure. Their self-esteem is very low, even though they may superficially hide this with bravado. It is much more rewarding to detect their qualities than to stick to and wear oneself out with their mistakes.

Example 22

Peter is a very difficult juvenile, cocooned within himself, and with very erratic behaviour. He barely answers, or if he does, it is in a very strange way. He steals and breaks the toy cars his friends have collected. At the institution for juveniles with behaviour disorders nobody knows what to do with him. He is not thought to be capable of anything, but considered as hopeless and barely fit for life. Yet one day an educator discovers his craft skills. He observes how Peter very skilfully fixes a toy car he has broken. The educator picks up the thread and asks: 'Would you like to help me fix something some time?'. From that moment, every time there is something to be fixed, Peter is called. He stays at the institution for five years, and when he leaves he finds a job as the operator of an excavator in a gravel pit. His behaviour is still quite difficult, but on his excavator he has a good chance of coping with his life.

For Peter it was a decisive step to discover that he was thought capable of something. In the perception of his carers his deficiencies faded into the background and they noticed more and more what was there: his craft skills and his interest in any kind of machines. This they tried to support and to encourage. Peter's example illustrates the importance of the next principle.

Not constantly staring at the 'symptom'

In dealing with 'difficult' persons there is a tendency to focus constantly on their 'problematic behaviour' and on trying, at any price, to change it. However, this staring at the 'symptom' usually has the opposite effect: the person will gradually be reduced to this behaviour, which thus will take on even more importance and with time suppress everything else. The 'symptom' will increasingly become the focus of attention for the disabled person too, until she finally identifies with it. Problematic behaviour and its effects will increase. The more this vicious circle turns, the less likely that something might change. This can often be observed with eating disorders: the more carers concentrate on changing a person's eating habits, the more *those* will become the focus of interest and the smaller the chance for a change.

It is essential to break the circle by looking beyond the symptom at *what is there too* and discovering the, perhaps tiny, signs for possible changes. Sometimes such signs even show in the disturbing behaviour itself when we try, instead of fighting it, to understand what it might express. There is always a long history to 'challenging behaviour' (and usually an equally long history of fighting it). That's why it is not possible to force quick changes. It takes time: the person repeatedly needs new and different experiences in order that change might slowly become possible.

Fostering a person's own way

People whose life is, to a high degree, determined by others usually feel a strong need to have their own way. When there is not much leeway for this need, it sometimes manifests in a person's sticking stubbornly to something the staff considers a minor detail, but is extremely important for this person. People with special needs may only vaguely feel the desire for autonomy and express it through rebellious and strange behaviour, which the carers may not understand.

Example 23
It is a dreadful, daily struggle for the staff to wake Anna. She complains, refuses to leave her bed, does not come down for breakfast and has to be forced eventually. Particularly with new staff members whose insecurity she senses, she goes to extremes with this fight. I suggest trying an alarm clock—it works. Anna gets up without any problem and is at breakfast on time. The alarm clock makes her feel that she is getting up on her own initiative and not because a staff member urges her to do so.

I prefer to talk about 'a person's own way' rather than about autonomy because, although there is common agreement that we have 'to foster the autonomy' of people with special needs, carers often have a clear agenda as to what those in their care should do 'autonomously'. Educators talk about autonomy in terms of how to 'bring adolescents to it', and it is often not very clear if it is the development of the young person they have in mind, or rather their own comfort. In relation to older people too, 'autonomy' is predominantly a matter of specific chores they should carry out themselves. What *they* want is rarely asked. What is called 'autonomy' quite often—unintentionally and very subtly—changes into to the opposite and becomes patronising. Yet to act independently sometimes means *not* to do what the carers expect or want. It is one of the paradoxes in social professions that these impulses must be backed up. They should not be considered as an offence, but welcomed as a sign of a person trying to find her own way. This has to be encouraged wherever possible.

For older people, to do it their own way may also occasionally mean staying in bed all day. For somebody with special needs it may mean not participating in a group excursion. *Autonomy always implies taking our own responsibilities.* This should be granted to a person wherever possible, even if she then does not act the way the carer thinks right.

Example 24

Ursina, 96, lives in a nursing home. Her thinking has remained very clear and she is happy to be still able to walk. Nevertheless she sometimes expresses the wish to die soon. Sometimes she refuses to eat, because she just does not feel like eating. The nurses regularly admonish her, 'If you don't eat, soon you will not be able to walk any more.' They know how important it is for Ursina to be able to walk, and hope that in this way they will motivate her to eat. But there are days when Ursina has a good appetite and enjoys her meal. There is no reason to patronise her and ignore the fact that on some days she does not feel like eating.

During puberty the need for independence and developing one's own ways is particularly strong. This is a basic difficulty in institutions for young people. In this period of growth adolescents have a hard time with fixed rules and the world of adults, and in addition they have to cope with the restricted structure of a school or institution. It is very understandable that adolescents at this age initially rebel against everything, no matter what it is. Sometimes they cannot even recognise where there is actually space for their own decision. They need time to come to terms with the structure; they have to explore its limits, perhaps even to kick against it and see if it really is solid. Only then will they be in a position to recognise the freedom they still have. It would be vain and counterproductive to interpret this as weird behaviour, bad intention or defiance.

It is not always easy to find the right balance. On the one hand adolescents need clear limits; on the other hand it is necessary for their development to oppose the adults and find their own ways. Educators often have a hard time understanding rebellion as a necessary aspect of growth, appropriate for this age. They feel offended, as they expect the adolescents to recognise that they are being helped and that it is good for them. They find it hard to accept the fact that most adolescents do not like to live in an institution.

Often the urge for independence appears in an extreme hairstyle or a way of dressing which hardly conforms to the standards of the educators. Hair particularly plays an important part in an adolescent's sense of identity and belonging. They usually react very badly when adults try to interfere on this point. It does not make much sense when an educator gives an ultimatum, 'By then you will have a haircut' or, 'As long as your hair is green you will not go out'. But perhaps a compromise can be agreed upon, such as at least an agreement to wash their hair. Basically, however, their appearance should be the responsibility of the adolescents themselves. They will make their experiences with it, and it is up to them if and whom they want to please.

Sometimes, with people showing behaviour disorders, behaviours which actually represent an individual choice are seen as a sign of decline or, with people with special needs, as an expression of their disability. On that score the state of a room is an inexhaustible issue. Ideas about tidiness and what a room should look like widely differ individually—even amongst educators. This individual choice should also be conceded to service users—of course within the limits of hygiene requirements. But within these limits, there has to be enough space to act individually. To foster a person's own way means also to offer clear and manageable choices.

Offering clear and manageable choices

It makes a difference for Frank's well-being in the old people's home if at breakfast he can choose his roll from the basket himself, rather than somebody putting it on his plate; it makes a difference if he can choose the jam he has a liking for right now, or if he is just given one by the carer. It makes a difference for Alice if she has something to say about when she wants to have her nails cut, or if the nurses decide that without her. These details may seem irrelevant, but they have an impact on how a person, whose freedom anyway is very restricted, feels. Therefore they are worth more attention being paid to them.

Yet a lack of choices may assume quite other dimensions and have much more serious effects.

Example 25
In a home for young people with behaviour disorders it is obligatory to participate at the official Christmas dinner with the board, the minister, and with speeches etc. Most youths don't like this event. But they have only the choice to either participate or make their get-away, with all the consequences this implies. Every year around Christmas several escapes take place.

To offer the young people some sensible alternatives from which they can choose—to organise the evening themselves in small groups or to have a celebration in the woods, for example—would allow them alternatives to running away. To avoid escapes with all their negative consequences for the young people, as well as for the whole community, certainly is much more desirable than having as many of them as possible, albeit unwillingly, participating at the official dinner.

Even for severely handicapped people who can act independently in only a very limited way, sometimes tiny possibilities can be found to let them make their own decisions, if only, for example, to choose their coffee cup themselves. The more restricted a person's life, the more demanding the challenge for the carers to find out where they can offer a tiny little bit of freedom for decisions. No matter how insignificant it may appear it is meaningful for the well-being of this person. On different levels and to a varying extent it is possible and necessary to offer choices. They improve life quality and reinforce self-esteem. Here too, an adequate balance between structure and self-determination has to be found. Choices have to offer real alternatives, yet they should not stress a person, but must *be clear and manageable for her* and adjusted to her individual capabilities.

Example 26

The carer in a small flat-sharing community for adults with special needs would like to motivate them not to spend every evening watching television, but to now and then turn to some other activity. All his attempts fail. If he asks the service users to make suggestions about how they could, once in a while, spend an evening differently, there is no response. Yet the social worker does not want to just organise a programme for them. A possible solution could be to agree with the group upon an evening when something else will be done, and to propose two or three concrete options from which they can choose.

In this example the social worker obviously expects too much as the leeway is too large for the service users. They need a support to keep it within manageable limits. This leads to another important principle in care-taking: support for independence.

Offering support to act independently

Instead of just assuming that a person is not able to do something and taking over from her, it would make more sense to offer her support allowing her, to some extent, to act independently. The envelopes for Herman's money (Example 5) and Anna's alarm-clock (Example 23) are examples of that. With John (Example 9) also, it would be worth exploring whether, with the help of a bowl, he could manage to measure how many carrots are needed for a salad. Or an educator could offer a young man help with tidying his room, showing him different ways to do it from which he could choose what suits him best. The idea of this kind of support is to back up a person if a task is too much for her, instead of just leaving her alone with it or taking it away from her. This way she experiences that, despite her restrictions, she is still able to do things by herself and does not just constantly fail. And the carers will thus perceive much more accurately where exactly the difficulties and limitations of a person are, where she needs support and where she is well able to act independently.

Example 27

Udo, a young man with learning disabilities, has got a new room. As he is quite independent, the carers leave it to him to unpack. He does it well and quickly, but at the end two big boxes remain lying around for weeks. Udo responds evasively to the requests of the social worker that he should finally empty the boxes and put his things into the cupboard. After a while, the social worker discovers that the boxes contain voluminous ship-models, which do not fit into the small cupboard, but would fit on the shelves where Udo has already put other belongings. It seems that he has unpacked the boxes one after the other without thinking about what will fit in where. Now he will have to take some things from the shelves and put them into the cupboard to make space for the ship-models. To make this connection is obviously too much for him. He is just able to see that there is no space left for his ship-models. The social worker helps Udo make the necessary changes.

It would be more sensible, together with Udo, to proceed step by step: trying out where the ships fit. They fit on the shelves, so they have to clear a space there and put some things away. They go into the empty cupboard. This way Udo participates in the process and is stimulated to deal with the problem in small portions. Moreover, this way the carer this way discovers *where exactly* Udo's difficulties lie and can offer him a support *at the point where he gets stuck.* Solving the problem is not simply taken away from Udo: he can still contribute. This is much more satisfying, not only for himself but also for the carer, as both can learn something out of it.

In homes for the elderly it is frequently observed that a meal is put in front of a person and, when she does not touch it, taken away after a while, often with the reproach, 'You did not eat again, Mrs X.' In this way carers overlook that older people, in a certain stage of decline, may still be able to make each single step—put the spoon into their mouth, swallow etc.—but may no longer be able to connect these steps. They need support, such as, 'Now you have to take the spoon', 'And now open your mouth', etc. The objection that this is too time-consuming does not justify the following examples, as experienced by a friend with her mother in a nursing home.

Example 28

The nurse puts a meal in front of Elizabeth, wishing her to enjoy it. When he comes later to clear away the tray, the meal is still untouched. The nurse: 'But Elizabeth, you don't want to eat again?'. Elizabeth: 'I would want to if I could.' The nurse, without a further word, takes the meal away.

It had definitely been the nurse's duty to find out what kind of support Elizabeth would need to be able to eat. Diagnostic information (like a neurological check-up) could make this task easier for the nurse. In no way can it be accepted that Elizabeth just does not eat, as she has clearly expressed that she would like to but cannot.

With others it is different. Some people (like Ursina in Example 24) in old age just like to eat very little. This too is an aspect of a person doing things her own way, which has to be respected. It is silly to urge her, and the reproach: 'You really have to eat' is out of place. Carers must be able to discern whether somebody does not eat because he has no appetite or because he can no longer manage it and needs support. This awareness is often missing in dealing with people in need of care—not only as far as eating is concerned.

Example 29

The nurse admonishes Elizabeth who is settled in an easy chair: 'You don't drink sufficiently, Elizabeth. If you do not drink, we will have to put you on a drip.' The visiting daughter has to draw the nurse's attention to the fact that the tea cup has been put on the bedside locker—out of Elizabeth's reach.

Frequently it is not only ignorance about the process of dementia but also thoughtlessness, stress or time pressure which causes such humiliating negligence, unnecessarily reinforcing the person's helplessness. It is imperative, on an organisational level, to establish the priorities differently and to take measures to avoid situations, as in the example described above. (One of several possibilities could be to mobilise volunteers to assist at meals.)

Giving clear information . . .

. . . particularly if it is something unpleasant, is a necessity. Only if *the general setting is transparent* is it possible to take decisions and to make choices. Carers firstly have to realise it clearly themselves, in order to make it clear for the people they take care of. The situation, as well as the outcome, must be transparent for everyone involved. Service users must not be outwitted or taken by surprise, even if this seems at first to be easier for the carer. The mistrust created this way is much more destructive than clear information, even if it may at first raise anxiety and resistance.

The other person needs time: time to take the information in, and time to react to it. There must be space for feelings to surface, and they have to be accepted. Only then will a person be ready to cope with the situation. It is an error to think that there is no time for this: as a rule, it is just a matter of a few minutes. Moreover, carers can avoid many a fight, refusal or panic reaction which would be considerably more time-consuming and destructive.

For many people—particularly for those with special needs—very simple situations, differing just a little from what they are used to, can be confusing and alarming. This is even more true for unusual events which they are not able to sort out. In such cases, some clarifying words describing the situation can be extremely helpful.

Example 30

Bernard has to go to the dentist. As he panics, this is always a difficult venture, aggravated by the unfavourably narrow position of his jaws. He can only be treated under anaesthetic, which raises even more panic. Though Bernard can barely hear, the new social worker in the evening explains to him in simple words exactly, step by step, what will happen tomorrow. (We will drive to town, see Doctor H. You will get an injection, then you will fall asleep,' etc.) The next day, Bernard, who usually reacts quite badly to much less relevant interruptions to his daily routine, without getting upset, patiently submits to the procedure.

Such information will not always be taken calmly. It may raise fear, irritation, anger and uncertainty. These feelings have to be expressed. It is very important that carers do not block or appease them, but allow and accept them empathically. At the same time they have to make it very clear that the facts conveyed by this information are not to be changed.

It is not always easy to accept the feelings of the other person while at the same time trying to get something done. This is equally true in educating children or in any situation where we have to ask another person to do something she does not like. We have a hard time hearing 'negative' reactions like anger, irritation and fear. We would like the other person *to be pleased* to meet our demands and we—consciously or unconsciously—send out this message. This way people are encouraged, or even trained, not to admit or show their feelings, even perhaps to not perceive them at all, or only with a bad conscience and then to oppress, repress, or rationalise them. That's why it is so important, whilst not losing sight of the given facts, to respond to feelings and to take them seriously.

Looking for the concrete

Besides responding to feelings and moods, there is another level we have to pay attention to: what are the *concrete* concerns at the bottom of a person's wish or complaint? Especially with big unrealisable wishes and global complaints about things which cannot be changed, it makes sense, together with these people, to find out more accurately what they really mean, what they actually dislike or miss. Sometimes it may be quite possible to take into account a specific aspect of a desire or a complaint and thus improve or relieve a situation which, as a whole, cannot be changed.

What does Hugo connect with the wish: 'I want to go home again'? Certainly it expresses how he feels after moving to the old people's home—homesick, sad, depressed or angry—and it is important to accept these feelings and take them seriously. But besides that, there may be a very concrete detail he misses or which is worrying him, which could easily be changed to make his life at the old people's home more pleasant. What is the concern behind Ruth's statement, 'I want to live somewhere else'? And what is it which depresses her colleague John, who categorically declares, 'I want a new job, I don't like it anymore at the workshop'? Perhaps it is not just a matter of general dissatisfaction, but also of concrete little things which could be changed. Only after carefully checking this can things be put right or a sensible solution found. Perhaps it is too noisy in Ruth's flat-sharing community and she needs an opportunity to withdraw. At the workshop John possibly does not get along with the man working next to him, and it would help him to change his place. To look for the concrete implies that 'impossible' desires are not just rejected, but taken seriously and checked to see if there is any solution. This in itself takes some of the strain off the people involved, and, at the same time, opens perspectives about how the concrete concerns could somehow, at least partially, be taken into account.

Example 31

A community for adults with special needs gets new furniture. The inhabitants choose it themselves. The shopping is done, and now everybody is busy setting up their rooms. All at once Mary flips and screams because the others have got a desk and she has not. She now urgently wants a desk, although when asked before she had always said that she did not want one. As she is entitled to a desk, and to stop the commotion—the transporter is still standing in front of the door— the social worker drives Mary back to the shopping centre to buy her a desk. After a week she discovers that it is still empty and Mary does not use it. It turns out that Mary needs a piece of furniture to put her cuddly toys in. For that, of course, the desk is not suitable. Yet Mary had not been able to figure that out. She just realised that there was no space for her cuddly toys and saw that the others had a desk, so she wanted to have one too.

It would have been wiser not to drive straight away to the shopping centre to meet Mary's desire, but first to find out: What *concretely* has she in mind? What does she need the desk for? And then to consider with her which piece of furniture would suit that best. Thus Mary's wish would have been met in a more sensible way and moreover she could have learned something from it.

To look for the concrete definitely has a growth-fostering aspect to it. It is not that people are always consciously aware of their concerns and just do not talk about them. Often they only realise what they actually want when the carers, by inquiring more thoroughly, can help them to find out.

Empathic imagination may even help to find out about concrete concerns of people who do not speak. By acting out different possibilities, the carer offers the other person an opportunity to react. From these reactions he may assume her concerns, provided he succeeds, to a certain extent, to enter her 'language'.

Finding the other person's language

This is an important condition of communicating with people with special needs. It is not sufficient for carers to *understand* the language of those they take care of; they also have to *express themselves in a way which will be understood by them.*

Sometimes carers do not realise how widely their language is determined by the professional jargon they picked up during their training and how far removed it is from the way people they take care of express themselves. Yet it is frightening how often they pick up this language. Those especially with a long history as psychiatric patients frequently speak of themselves in perfect terms of psychopathology which have nothing to do with what they are experiencing.

It is not just a matter of avoiding professional jargon but, above all, of finding a language the other person can understand and which is close to her experiencing. To find the language of another person implies and— *'language' here does not just mean the verbal expression, but a person's whole way of expressing herself* —explaining, making visible, describing things in a way the other person can grasp and understand. With one person, images may be appropriate; another may need logical explanations. It is not always just a matter of 'the right words', but sometimes also of 'the right gestures'. To find another person's language can also mean taking her by the hand and doing something together.

On the other hand, a person's helplessness and speechlessness must not mislead carers to underestimate her receptivity to language. With a severely disabled woman who could not speak, a therapist discovered that she actually *did* react to language. She screwed up her face when the therapist said, 'I have to go now', or smiled when she promised, 'I'll see you tomorrow'. We do not know *what* this woman could take in. Was it the intonation, the emotional quality of what was said, or could she really, sometimes (she did not always react) understand words? However, *something sometimes* reached her. This shows that it makes sense to talk to people who do not speak, because there is a chance that they will pick up something, and even if this may not always happen it would be a failure not to take the chance.

Also, with severely physically and mentally impaired older people who can no longer express themselves and apparently do not understand, we have to talk in a way that respects their dignity. It is a shame, which can never be justified, that there are still institutions where older people are called 'grandma' and 'grandpa'. To talk *about* persons who are present instead of *with* them is equally unacceptable. I experienced this with a friend who died early and in her last years had to live in a nursing home.

Another painful and humiliating habit is when patients are talked to as if they were not grown-up.

Example 32

Nina, 50, has multiple sclerosis. The disease has progressed in such a way that she not only cannot move but also cannot talk anymore. She has practically no means left to express herself. Yet when I visit her, I see in her eyes that she sensitively takes in what I am saying and is pleased when issues she has always been interested in are touched on. She is a very cultured woman who worked as an art critic before becoming ill. It hurts to hear the nurses talk to her in baby language. And I can see in Nina's eyes that she definitely feels humiliated by this situation.

Knowing something about a patient's background could help nurses to strike the right note with people who cannot express themselves any more. However, the most important approach to the language of another person is *listening with all senses,* as has been described at the beginning of this chapter.

Recognising one's own part

In order to be able to solve problems and cope with critical situations, it is indispensable for carers to recognise the way their own personalities and experiences are reflected in their actions. The complex way that personality or personal problems can have an impact on somebody's work are a very important issue for carers, which will be dealt with in Chapter 6. In the context of these guidelines for everyday work I am talking very pragmatically of different aproaches and of the simple fact that every person involved, including the carer, has a part to play in every situation. To recognise clearly one's own part is crucial; not for the insight of 'having done something wrong' or to 'feel guilty', but in order to discover and try new ways to proceed. Sometimes, in a stressful situation, this is the only concrete clue that something needs to change, and it usually gets a carer further than the—mostly vain—attempt to change the other person. This is particularly true for difficult situations, which escalate or happen over and over again in a similar way.

The question: 'What can *I* change in this situation?' helps to overcome helplessness and enables positive action. We can always change *something* in our own behaviour. Here, too, it is helpful to *look for the concrete*, for clues to calm a situation or to avoid its escalation. How did this argument start? What exactly did I say? To what did the other person react so angrily? etc. Often external conditions have an influence too: Were we alone or was somebody else present? Was the door open or closed? Was it noisy? etc. Very banal details may indicate how the carer can *somewhat* change the situation and thus give the other person a chance to also behave *somewhat* differently.

For example, it has a quite different effect if a carer, when feeding a lame, speechless man who is resisting, tries to force the full spoon between his lips, or if she takes the spoon only after first giving him a chance to open his mouth himself. What is appropriate with one person may not be suitable for another. It is definitely worth trying different possibilities. Even if the other person is not in a position to take this little chance to change something, it is already an improvement if the carer, by changing her own way of being, *makes the situation easier for herself.* This, too, contributes to easing the tension and may open ways to improve the situation further for everybody involved.

In the following I shall point to a methodical means, which in many different ways is helpful in nearly all areas mentioned above.

Reflecting the situation

On emotional and sensory levels it is useful, as we have seen, to respond to a person's experiencing, or to help her to be more aware of it, by saying, for example, 'You don't like it when your hands get wet.' 'You are sad because nobody came to visit you today.' On a factual level, to reflect the situation may help the people involved to understand it

Signpost 2   Recognising one's own part

A: In daily life
For example, when difficult situations escalate, or happen repeatedly and things seem to go round in circles, change your own behaviour or try something new in order to enable the other person to act differently.

B: On a personal level
Be consciously aware of your own feelings, reactions, likes and dislikes, and set them aside.
Watch out for your blind spots, in order to not be at their mercy, but stay open to the other person.

better, for example, 'It is very noisy here, because the carpenter is fixing the door.'

To reflect the situation also helps to bring a fraught situation to another level from where it is perhaps easier to find a way to calm it.

Reflect the situation, especially when:
• conversations turn in circles
• power fights are going on
• aggression escalates.

This is likely to break through the vicious circle. We could also say such things as: 'We are talking very loud now', 'I say you have to wash your hair today, you say no', 'You don't like it when it is so noisy outside', 'You feel very much like going for me right now', 'You are angry, and I am impatient', 'You are irritated that the meal is served now', etc. To reflect it lessens the tension of a situation, as it is simply stated and, for the time being, accepted as it is.

Reflections are sometimes misunderstood as a mechanical 'mirroring technique'. This is not at all what they are meant to be. Reflecting the situation well must be based on congruence and empathic understanding of how the other person feels. There are moments when it is not appropriate and the other person just has to be left alone. But this, too, is only possible when the carer breaks the circle, pauses for a moment and considers the situation for himself.

Reflecting the situation has to be motivated by the wish to understand and accept the other person and to communicate this to her. What is essential is the attitude behind it: it is not a matter of making a fool of or blaming somebody, but of clarifying and understanding the situation. If this comes through, changes may become possible. And it also gives the carer a breather which enables him to step back, to break the vicious circle, to stop the escalation and thus *at least to change his own part in the cycle.*

To reflect the situation can also be useful with people who don't speak: it helps the carer to step back and clarify the situation for herself—perhaps the other person who does not use language can sense that in some way.

In Garry Prouty's Pre-Therapy, which will be introduced in Chapter 9, this principle is further developed and differentiated into a method to make contact with severely disabled and contact-impaired persons.

Practical foundations and guidelines for everyday work represent helpful signposts for the individual carer, as well as for team meetings, to find out where the problem might come from and what should be changed (see Signpost 1 on p. 17 and 3 below).

Signpost 3   Guidelines for everyday work

Listen

Take the other person seriously

Comparing with 'normality'

Stay with the obvious

Don't let your guide be what you already know

Facilitate and respond to a person's experiencing

Encourage

Don't constantly stare at the 'symptom'

Foster a person's own way

Offer clear and manageable choices

Offer support to act independently

Give clear information

Look for the concrete

Find the other person's language

Recognise your own part

Reflect the situation

5

Specific aspects of care for people with special needs[1]

In connection with the guidelines described in the last chapter, there are some additional aspects to pay attention to when working with people with moderate to severe mental disabilities.

Fostering a person's contact with her own experience

For many of them, to be in contact with their own experiencing is very difficult and *actually has to be stimulated by the carers*. Unfortunately, though not intentionally, the education of children with special needs often tends to foster incongruence more than congruence. Very rarely during their growth are they encouraged to trust their feelings, as these are often expressed in a bizarre, unintelligible way. As a rule, people around them do not make much effort to understand those odd behaviours, but spend lots of energy on stopping them.

Because of this they learn, more than others, to suppress or even be unaware of their feelings. As we all know, this is possible only to some degree, and pent-up emotions will occasionally break out all the more violently and inappropriately. A person with special needs will become overwhelmed by such an outburst, unable to handle it, feel scared and guilty. The carers react even more rigidly, and the vicious circle is completed.

While more severely mentally handicapped people usually express their feelings more, though sometimes by bizarre behaviours, this is much harder for the moderately disabled. In this respect the desire to appear 'normal' plays a sinister role: sinister because it leads people with special needs to too much adjustment and cuts them off from their emotions. Concerned about not appearing handicapped, they only show 'positive' and adjusted feelings. In no way do they want to admit that they feel worried, irritated or angry, out of fear that these feelings might be labelled 'not normal'. And people around them, whether intentionally or not, reinforce this tendency. Well-adjusted people with special needs who appear 'normal' are easier to deal with than those who are rebellious and let out their feelings—mostly by odd and unintelligible ways of

1. Special needs in this chapter refer particularly to people with moderate to severe mental disabilities. See p. 2, 'The use of language in this book'.

behaving. It is easily overlooked that there is often a high price to pay for such apparently 'normal' behaviour. The person is not in contact with her emotions and her perception of self, already not very strong, weakens even more.

Example 33

Irene, a woman of 60, who is in therapy with me, expresses her feelings mostly in indirect ways by accusing others. Only after several years can she express how irritated and angry she feels, because her cousin talks to her as if she were a child. Up to then, she had only dared to criticise him for not speaking the dialect spoken in his native area, but having taken on the dialect of his wife. This was the language of Irene's childhood, which she hated and had refused to speak ever since her mother died and she had been moved to another town.

Irene could not admit the anger against her cousin as her own subjective feeling, but had to find some apparently 'objective wrong behaviour' in order to justify her criticism. We frequently observe this kind of shift, and not only in people with special needs. Recalling the theory of the self-concept (p.12), we can easily assess the impact this splitting off of her feelings and experiences has on her growth. To have little or no contact with one's own emotions is one of the main reasons for psychological disorders and for difficulties in coping with life.

People with special needs usually mistrust their own experience because repeatedly it has been misunderstood and dismissed as inadequate or unrealistic by the people around them. Sometimes this goes so far that they are not even aware of how they experience and sense things, but fall back on platitudes and on what they hear others say.

Example 34

When I ask Irene if she likes the new job at the workshop, she answers, 'I always work hard.' Or when the question is discussed whether, because of her age, she would like to stop working or prefer to continue, she says, 'At the workshop they still appreciate my help.'

I can only try, again and again, to gently stimulate Irene's contact with her own experiencing: 'You were pleased', 'You don't like this so much', 'Now it gets too much for you'. The hope is that this will slowly open up this dimension and make it more accessible for her, yet above all, not add even more to her distance from her feelings and sensations.

Quite ordinary everyday situations can be used to call someone's attention to the experiencing quality, and also to the fact that this is not the same for everybody: 'You don't like rain. Anna enjoys the rain,' 'You get scared when he laughs like this', 'You don't like the noise of the vacuum cleaner, Mark likes it', etc.

A crucial factor is how carers deal with their own feelings, as it has a model function for those in their care and helps them better to perceive and express their feelings themselves. This is particularly true for 'negative' feelings like anger, rage, irritation, weariness etc. It is important for people with special needs to see that carers too are sometimes angry, depressed, or sad, and that they admit these feelings. This makes it easier for them to accept such feelings in themselves. Of course, it has to happen in a constructive way. Carers must not use their feelings to pressure persons in their care or to make them feel guilty, but give an example of how such emotions are part of being human and can be lived with and expressed without being overwhelmed.

People with special needs usually have a hard time accepting 'negative' feelings; they feel guilty when, nevertheless, these break through.

Example 35

Armin tells me about a fierce argument he had with his boss at the workshop this afternoon. He accuses himself bitterly of 'not being able to explain things in a way people can understand'. When I ask him if he was irritated because Mrs H did not understand him, he gives me a startled look and says, 'But one should not think such a thing'. During another session he expresses his fears of 'flipping' during the coming vacation because this had happened during the last vacation. He had been tired of being away, did not feel good any more and had wished to go home. 'I have to tell myself, this time always be happy,' he firmly declares. I try carefully to help him understand that it is impossible to just be happy all the time, and that perhaps it would be better to tell the facilitators when he feels homesick or depressed, instead of swallowing it and then probably 'flipping' precisely because of that.

This example, once more, demonstrates how essential it is that carers empathically pay attention to, and accept, those moods and feelings. Often they have a hard time with it, because they try their best and feel responsible for the well-being of the people they take care of. This responsibility is more than they can cope with: even the best possible caring cannot prevent somebody occasionally not feeling well or being sad or annoyed. If carers are aware of this it not only helps the concerned person, but also contributes to avoiding escalations and dramatic outbursts which are unpleasant and sometimes scaring for everybody. Moreover, in this way people with special needs learn to be more aware of their feelings. It is a process which takes time: it takes more time the greater a person's alienation from her experiencing, the roots of which often go back to childhood. By encouraging children to be aware of, and to accept, their emotions and experiences the early years could have different outcomes.

But it is not just in terms of their emotions that people with special needs have few opportunities to build up self-confidence. In matters of daily life too, again and again, they experience 'I cannot do it', or 'I am doing it the wrong way'. This marks their self-concept in a way that makes them forget how to trust their experience, and they orientate themselves exclusively on what is communicated to them as 'adequate'. And, as there are indeed many things they cannot do, or they do the wrong way, their behaviour from early on is constantly corrected. Sometimes this is done much more than necessary, because people around them wish them to appear as 'normal' as possible, forgetting how important it is that people with special needs, wherever possible, try out their own ways, even if their behaviour then may not quite conform to the norm. They already have to be corrected more than enough in situations where it is indeed impossible for them to follow their impulses. So they increasingly forget how to perceive their own impulses, sensations and reactions or dismiss them straightaway as 'not normal'.

Stimulating a person's own impulses

With a mentally handicapped person, it is not enough to just support her independence; her own impulses have actually to be stimulated and encouraged. Daily life offers countless opportunities to do so. Clothing, for example, is an important area. It is alarming how sometimes, from the way people with special needs are dressed, the taste of the staff can be detected.

Example 36

Lucy is very concerned to dress in a way that pleases people around her. On weekends, when she goes home, she dresses to reflect her mother's taste (which is considered awful by the staff); on weekdays she wears the clothes she thinks would please the staff. Looking at her wardrobe, it is easy to make out which piece of clothing has been bought with which staff member.

The staff could counteract this by not just being content when their clients adapt to their taste, but encouraging them to find out *what they like themselves.* For example, instead of saying: 'This sweater does not go with the trousers you wear', they could let Lucy look in the mirror and try out with her: 'How do you like yourself better, this way or that way?'. It is necessary to emphasise, again and again, that not everybody has to have the same taste, for instance by saying: 'I like this one, John likes the other one, which one do you like?'.

Example 37

In an adult education programme for people with special needs, the participants do a role-play on how to buy clothes. A week later, Paul's mother tells the facilitator that she had to buy Paul a dark sweater for a funeral. They went from shop to shop, and finally Paul had to decide between two sweaters. Both the mother and the shopkeeper suggested the darker one, which would better suit the occasion and in which they thought Paul looked better. But Paul insisted on the other, a flashy, bright blue sweater. Asked why, he said, 'Because it feels so soft when I touch it'.

To provide such experiences does not necessarily need external programmes. It can easily be integrated into the social activities of the organisation or community. For example, entertaining and yet instructive play with clothes and cloths could be arranged, offering people an opportunity to try out, to look in a mirror, to look at each other and to share their different tastes. This could be a relaxing as well as exciting alternative to the, sometimes rather hectic and overloaded, leisure programmes provided for the residents.

These programmes could be built more upon the idea of *providing opportunities for experiences and developing people's awareness of their own sensations, tastes and opinions.* Any excursion or shopping trip may help to stimulate individual perceptions and views. People with special needs usually have a strong tendency to adapt to what is considered 'nice'. This should not be reinforced: instead they should be encouraged not to immediately dismiss as 'not normal' what they perceive and feel, but to take it seriously, even if it is different from how they think it should be.

By this I do not mean that the fact of being disabled should be denied or covered up. It is a reality to be accepted, yet a reality with many different facets which are easily overlooked if our eyes remain fixed on the label 'special needs'.

The attitude towards being disabled . . .

. . . is a complex problem with which people with special needs are constantly confronted—sometimes in quite contradictory ways. On the one hand their carers would like to see them as much 'adapted' as possible, and on the other hand they are expected to accept their being disabled. This is no small demand on people who, being disabled, are perhaps therefore not in a position to meet such an expectation. Especially, as wherever they go they are confronted with discrimination; at stores, on the bus, at the swimming pool, on the street. No wonder many of them tend to deny, as much as they can, their being handicapped, and try to keep a distance from other people with special needs. For more severely disabled people it seems easier, because they are probably less conscious of their being handicapped. But they, too, are very sensitive to the reactions of other people and do sense that they are not how they 'should' be.

In this respect again, *the attitude of the carers* has a crucial impact. It largely determines how people they take care of can live with their impairments. To accept it is possible only if they can also experience *positive aspects* of their being as they are. For that they need support and encouragement from the carers, and this requires *being able to see* such positive aspects.

To take people seriously does not mean overlooking their handicaps, but *taking them seriously with their handicaps.* In the effort—in itself commendable—not to discriminate against people with special needs, this is sometimes forgotten. Undifferentiated 'political correctness' can have the opposite effect to what has been intended, as the following example demonstrates.

Example 38
Nineteen-year-old Betty lives with her parents. She spends three days a week in a day care facility offering special programmes for people with special needs, and

on two days she goes to school. From where she lives, there is no public transport to these places, therefore the social services so far had paid for a taxi. But with ongoing financial restrictions, these contributions will be cut and other solutions have to be found. Together with her parents, Betty is invited to a meeting. As she is over 18, she has a right to be informed personally and to give her view. The social worker has prepared a paper which describes the situation and which, for half an hour, she tries to explain to Betty in detail. She does not realise that Betty is neither able to follow these explanations nor able to listen for such a long stretch of time. Yet, when asked if she did understand, Betty's answer is 'yes'. Several alternatives to the actual situation are discussed. After that Betty is asked again if she did understand, and again she says 'yes'. The social worker does not realise that Betty did not understand anything and just said 'yes' because she felt awkward and wanted to bring the situation to an end. At home, when asked by her mother why she had said 'yes', Betty says, 'What else could I do?', which shows how, emotionally, she had quite accurately grasped the situation she was in. As it turns out, the only result of the meeting is that Betty now thinks she cannot go to the day care facility any more. She is very upset and desperate, because she likes it there and sees the facility as her second home.

This despair could have been spared Betty if the social worker had not only taken into account her being old enough, but also her limited ability to understand. Although acting with the best of intentions and wanting to take Betty seriously, she definitely lacked the necessary empathy in Betty's frame of reference. Yet, without this empathy, the particular requirements of people with special needs cannot be met. To expect too much of them is as counter-productive as to not believe in them enough. Again, it is a matter of finding an adequate balance, which for each person is different.

People with special needs, like everybody else, have to learn how to live with their weak sides. But carers must also make it possible for them to experience and recognise their strong sides and capabilities. Emphasis should not be so much on the label 'special needs' as on individual *strengths and weaknesses*—their own and those of others, including the carers—and on learning to deal with them. To recognise that other people have their specific capabilities and limitations too, to discover that human beings are different and to learn to accept these differences, is an imperative condition for a tolerable way in which people with special needs can live with each other and with the people around them.

We do need to discriminate between different kinds and grades of disabilities, but we should be very careful about using labels such as more handicapped, less handicapped, stronger than others, weaker than others. People with special needs tend to adopt these labels themselves to categorise each other and to establish a hierarchy of handicaps and disabilities in which they see themselves as high up as possible. This, of course, does not foster good relations with each other.

Example 39

For Irene, the degree to which the other women in her group are disabled is very important. She is very happy to say of one of her friends, 'She belongs to the weaker group', or of another, 'She gets fits and has to take medication, I don't'. It was terrible for her when a few years ago, after an accident, she had to move to a group of more severely disabled women. It is not relevant for her if she feels better or worse there: what counts is the stigma, 'I now belong to a weaker group.'

It is disturbing to see, as in the example above, the negative effects this sort of labelling can have. It would be much more constructive if carers would try to encourage people who have to live together to be aware of and to tolerate differences in human beings, and to show this awareness and tolerance by example. People with disabilities must be encouraged to benefit from their strengths and to balance the weak sides of each other. They should be given opportunities to look at their own strengths and those of others and to see where they *need* help and where they *can offer* help to others. In addition to mutual help, this attitude facilitates independence from the carers and stimulates friendship among people with special needs.

Yet for all this stressing positive aspects, we cannot ignore *that they sometimes suffer deeply from being disabled* even if they cannot always express it as clearly as in the following example.

Example 40

Elsa, usually a lively and cheerful woman, during the therapy session suddenly bursts out, crying bitterly: 'I wish I could fly away like a little bird, far far away . . . and nothing . . . nothing at all . . . only whistle nice little songs . . . I am a dirty rag . . . just a dirty rag . . . I am nothing, nothing, nothing . . . nothing at all, that's what I am.' To try to comfort and appease her is out of place. The only thing I can do is to respond to her feelings and bear them with her until they ease and there is room again for other things. I am strongly aware of my helplessness and feel a little embarrassed as Elsa, after the session, hugs me and says, 'You really helped me.'

This example, once more, clearly demonstrates how essential it is in such a situation to just empathically be there and support the person. Carers often have a hard time just to 'be there'. Such emotional outbursts from their clients strongly confront them with their own helplessness and limitations. To 'be there' is not an easy task, but in those situations it helps a person more than anything else, because it makes space for her emotions and encourages her to express them.

It is not pleasant to be handicapped—this fact cannot be denied or whitewashed. The people affected feel this very painfully now and then, even if not many of them are able to express it as impressively as Elsa did. Yet those who cannot express themselves verbally probably sometimes have similar feelings. How does a woman feel who is hardly able to move, and cannot speak and eat by herself? Could it be an expression of her distress about this condition not to open her mouth and to refuse being fed by a new carer she does not know? We do not know, but depend on empathic guesses to get an idea of what could be going on within her.

In this respect our own feelings may serve as a signpost. Carers too, in some situations, feel helpless, sad, angry, weary, disgusted and may curse the fact that people have to live with such handicaps. Usually such feelings and thoughts are suppressed because they 'should not be'. But as suppressed feelings are not controllable and will, at some point, break through anyway, this helps neither the carers nor the people they take care of, who are thus confirmed in having to hide their feelings. Whereas if carers are consciously aware of those emotions in themselves, not only will their psychological well-being benefit, but they may also discover a means for better understanding the person who has given rise to those feelings.

Sexuality and relationships

In this area, people with special needs particularly experience the distress of being disabled. Although, fortunately, the attitude towards their sexuality has become much more liberal in the last few decades, the question if and how they can have relationships and acknowledge their sexuality remains a difficult and often insoluble problem. Even if these feelings are tolerated or encouraged by the community they live in, the possibilities are still limited. Various factors play their part; including society, philosophy, personality, personal development, the actual situation etc. Is it possible at all, in everyday life, to deal with this complex issue in a person-centred way?

It is a tight-rope walk, in the area of relationships, to handle structure and self-determination in a way that respects individual freedom and the right for love, friendship and sexuality of a disabled person and at the same time protects her from dangers like violence, AIDS, unwanted pregnancy etc. There is no magic formula. Each person, each situation, is different and has to be carefully looked at and thought over.

First we have to clarify what those concerned really want. What do they expect of a relationship, what are their options, and what is the general setting? We have to find out sensitively and individually what *concretely* a person is looking for. Carers have a tendency to transfer their own ideas and ideals of relationships onto the people they take care of, and to work from standards which are not always fit for them. If even 'normal' couples are only rarely able to really meet such high ideals, how difficult must it be for people with special needs! Although in terms of relationships their desire to 'be normal' is particularly strong, and notions like 'going steady', 'being engaged', or 'being married' have a nearly magic attraction, it is often not at all clear what they specifically have in mind. Therefore it is not of much use to force their relationships into norms which often even 'normal' couples don't think they can cope with. How should people with special needs be expected to meet such high ideals— apart from the fact that often it is not what they really need? These real needs should first be carefully clarified.

Instead of talking of 'going steady', of engagement or even marriage, and then leaving it to them to come to terms with the ideas they connect with these notions, alternatives should be developed. Here again, it is helpful to look for the concrete. What exactly do these two people expect from their relationship? What would they like and what would they not like? Where do the expectations of both partners conform and where do they differ? Carers should, together with those concerned, carefully find that out, and then look for other ways in which these two people could handle their relationship, according to their specific needs and possibilities. The most important thing is to stay absolutely *concrete and pragmatic*, and not to let oneself be guided by ideas of how it 'should' be.

Example 41

Erna and Eric 'go steady'. Soon Eric wants to 'break it off'. The carers try to talk him out of that. They are afraid it could be a bad setback for Erna 'not to go with Eric anymore'. The consultant suggests that the carers should find out from Eric what exactly it means for him 'not to go together anymore'. What is it concretely that Eric does not want? It turns out that Eric feels pressed when Erna, without asking, comes to his room whenever she likes. (For Erna this is part of 'going steady'). But he still likes to kiss and cuddle and go out with her sometimes. Instead of a fixed 'either/or', 'go steady' or 'break off', other ways have to be found and clear agreements made for their being together, for example, going out with each other once or twice a week. And Erna should not just go into Eric's room, but ask him if it is okay and accept that he may sometimes say no. Eric, on the other hand, should not just wait for Erna to ask and then say yes or no, but occasionally ask Erna himself if she would like to come to his room.

The structure of an organisation or community can provide a sheltered space where various forms of relationship are possible, according to the needs of the inhabitants. To find out concretely and clearly what two persons want from each other and what they don't want, and make the respective agreements, is far more constructive than the label 'engaged' or 'going steady', not least because, when needs change, these agreements can be modified without inevitably leading to breaking off the relationship. Moreover, in this way people with special needs learn to recognise more clearly and more specifically what they really want, instead of sticking to a status like 'engaged' or 'married'—a status which is likely to develop a momentum of its own, too difficult for them to live up to.

Example 42

John and Liz are engaged. They are very proud of it, as it has been duly celebrated in the institution and grants them a higher status. Soon, together with another roommate, Werner, they can form a small flat-sharing community and move to their own apartment. This is the beginning of difficulties. It is the rule in flat-sharing communities that all inhabitants, men and women, have to share the housework equally. John shirks whenever he can; he is engaged now, and in his mind it is the woman's task to do the housework for both. Liz thinks so too, so she does the housework for them all, as Werner does not see either why he, as a man, should do housework when John does not. Even though the carers try to counteract these traditional male–female roles, as soon as they leave the house, Liz, without a word, takes over the tasks of the men. Although she feels that this is how it has to be, very soon it gets too much for her, and she often gets bad-tempered or depressed. And soon John's sexual demands too get too much for her, and she wishes she had her own room again. But for a long time she does not dare to say so because, for her, it means to 'break off the engagement'—a humiliating failure in her eyes. For a long time the term 'engagement' was in the way of any change and hindered a solution being found to which both could agree and which matched their changed needs.

They would have more easily come to terms with the changes in their relationship, which for them were connected with the stigma of 'breaking off the engagement', if they could have worked out other, more appropriate ways of being together. As mildly handicapped people, in particular, have so much longing to be like 'normal people', they experience twice the sense of failure when they cannot cope with what counts as the norm.

The wish to be in a relationship is not always a matter of sexuality, nor is the desire for sexual contact always connected with a need to be in a close relationship. Here again, carers should put aside their own values and find out what it is *exactly* the people concerned want.

The idea is still prevalent that people with special needs are particularly sex driven. This is very rarely true. Experience shows that many of them are much more interested in closeness, tenderness, touching and cuddling than in sexual intercourse. However, there are of course others who enjoy and feel a need for sexual contacts, be it within or without a steady relationship.

Example 43

Daisy, a 30-year-old woman with Down's Syndrome is in therapy with me. At a meeting the carers express their concern because Daisy has apparently more or less been forced into sexual contact by a friend. I am somewhat surprised because Daisy, talking of this friend, has never mentioned such an incident, nor has she, in any way, appeared distraught or depressed. In the next session I cautiously ask questions. It turns out that, for some time, when she used to see her friend regularly, they did have sexual contact, which Daisy did not dislike at all. On the contrary, she very much enjoyed these physical sensations and is disappointed that she is no longer allowed to visit her friend as often as before. But from the way she was brought up, as well as from the reactions of the carers, she feels that she has done something 'bad'. She does not dare to admit her pleasure in these sexual contacts, but claims that they happened against her will. She has clearly anticipated what the carers want to hear her say. For them, sexual contacts are unacceptable outside a stable relationship. They do not see that Daisy was neither interested in, nor probably up to, such a relationship, but simply enjoyed the sexual experience.

Opinions are divided on whether such relations can, or have to be, tolerated. I don't think that we have the right just to transfer our own ideas of morality and values on to people with special needs, thus restricting their already limited opportunities in this area even more. Our own standards and feelings regarding relationships vary. And I think we should accept that theirs do too.

People with special needs have so little opportunity to experience their sexuality that we should not deny them the few chances that come up, as long as it does not intimidate or endanger anybody. We also need to be tolerant towards compensations like fetishism or sex magazines etc. But the consideration that nobody else gets harmed and the safety of the persons concerned should be the criteria for tolerating or not tolerating a situation; not the personal values of the carers.

To protect this safety is not an easy task. Taking AIDS into consideration and increasing sexual violence, it is not enough just to provide contraception. Restrictions cannot always be avoided. And again, mildly handicapped people, who particularly resent restrictions, are most affected.

Example 44
Sabina, a 44-year-old woman with a mild mental disability, lives in a flat-sharing community. She loves to go out in the evening and frequent pubs where they play music. She feels good there, not only because she likes the music, but also because in this milieu she is not so much noticed as being disabled. There does not seem to be much difference between her and the other people there, and she is treated as an equal. One night she comes home, rather excited, and reports to the carer that a man had wanted to invite her to his home, but that she did not go. Quite obviously, she would have liked to, but was not sure if it was 'allowed'. The carer too is not sure how to react. She does not want to patronise Sabina, but she is afraid that something could happen. There is a risk that a man who approaches her in a pub could get violent once she goes home with him. She relays her fears to Sabina who promises that in the future she will never go home with a man. The carer does not feel good about the way she handled the situation. She has the impression that she manipulated Sabina and that the problem was not satisfactorily resolved.

As the carer, at that moment, could not think of any solution, it was certainly congruent to admit her fears. But probably, in the long run, other solutions should be found. For example, a rule could be set that new acquaintances should first be invited to the community for a coffee or a meal, so that carers get to know them and can form an impression. The fact that he does or does not accept such an invitation in itself is a statement. But there is, of course, no guarantee and risks can never be totally excluded.

For the carers it is a balancing act between taking risks in order to respect the personal freedom of someone with special needs, making relationships possible for her and imposing the necessary restrictions to protect her from dangers. Besides, carers are often bound by legal regulations. Yet restrictions based upon real necessities are definitely more honest and easier to cope with, even if they are painful, than restrictions based on the personal standards of the carers, often not understandable for the people they take care of.

The difficult demands of living in a group

To live in a group, particularly if it is not chosen, makes high demands on the social capabilities of people with special needs. This paradox is not usually sufficiently considered. On the one hand they are declared handicapped and limited in their social capabilities, and on the other hand they are quite naturally expected to adjust, have regard and understanding for the people they have to live with—to a degree most 'normal' people would hardly be willing to achieve.

To find their way in the group takes up a lot of a person's energy and learning ability—resources they otherwise might use better for their personal growth. Moreover, what has been achieved after considerable effort is, time and again jeopardised by a new situation (such as new residents or new staff members). Such a change requires new adjustments and makes new demands. This is asking much of people who otherwise are not credited with much capability, and it is amazing what they can achieve in this respect. But sometimes they are just totally stressed. This is often the real root of much inadequate behaviour, panicking or 'flipping'. It would be wise, sometimes, to lower the demands and look for solutions which would take some strain off the person, even if this does not conform with 'group ideals', which are usually based more on the theoretical ideas of the carers than on the real needs of the people they take care of.

I increasingly ask myself if it would not suit some people with special needs better to live in *a sort of boarding house where they are looked after individually,* instead of having to live in a group which is not beneficial for everybody. Of course residents of such a boarding house should not just be left to fend for themselves. There should be programmes for common leisure activities in which they could choose to participate if they want to. Intense, but not necessarily time-consuming, individual care has to be built in. Carers could, for example, at fixed times, be present and available to listen to and, if necessary, help and consult residents. This could also offer new challenges and allow other priorities for the carers, who often complain that they need too much time and energy to organise routines and settle conflicts in the group and that there is not enough space for individual care.

Such ideas are certainly no magic formula. Each way of living has its specific problems. Yet, I believe that, in addition to existing concepts, options as described above could be useful and really meet the needs of many adult, particularly older, people with special needs.

6
Consequences for carers

What are the specific demands of person-centred work? What effect does this attitude have on the self-image of carers and on their relationships with the people they take care of? And how do they themselves benefit from working this way?

The relationship to the clients

The relationship between carers and clients is fundamental not only for the person-centred approach. There is common agreement that it is a major aspect of social work. Yet ideas of how this relationship should be differ widely and are sometimes not very clear. It is worth thinking about more thoroughly.

From a person-centred point of view the relationship between carers and clients (just like the therapeutic relationship in client-centred therapy) is based on empathy, acceptance and congruence. Congruence requires that the specific characteristics of this relationship, as well as its limitations, have to be clear and transparent for everybody involved. It is, to some degree, a one-sided relationship where the priority is on the clients' well-being and on encouraging their independence. *Their* needs must be met, *their* living spaces created, not those of the carers whose private life takes place elsewhere.

For the staff *it is a job* living with people with special needs or in need of care. After work they go back to their homes and live their own private lives. This fact is frequently blurred: carers try to establish a very close personal relationship with clients and raise desires they cannot meet. Very soon they may be burnt out and have to look for another job. For people with special needs this means, once more, that they are abandoned and disappointed—an experience they know only too well. Depending on their different personalities, they try in different ways to protect themselves from such let-downs; some by persistently clinging to the carers in the hope that this will hold them; others, on the contrary, by refusing any relationship and resisting the closeness the carers try to offer them.

It becomes particularly problematic when carers use the relationship with their clients to meet their own unfulfilled needs or unsolved problems. Whether those needs are for recognition, closeness, affection, tenderness, power, the unrealised wish for their own children or other aspects of life carers did not come to terms with, to transfer it onto people they take care of is definitely an abuse (even when there is no sexual harassment involved—which unfortunately happens sometimes too).

Example 45

In a nursing school, teachers are on very friendly terms with their students. They are tolerant, do not pressure their performance, show an interest in their personal difficulties and, after school hours, frequently socialise with them. Then the exams come up, and the students are flabbergasted as, all of a sudden, the teachers are not that understanding any more but severely judge and grade their performances. Instead of, right from the start, making clear demands, the teachers, by being too friendly, have blurred the fact that, under the circumstances of the exams, the relationship could not be equal, as they have to grade the students and make decisions that affect their future.

More distance would have been more appropriate to the situation and ultimately more helpful for the students. It is a fatal misunderstanding to confuse the person-centred attitude with simply 'being nice'. Congruence, amongst other things, entails not blurring a professional context.

In this work, *a reliable professional relationship,* which keeps some distance but provides continuity, is far more honest. It serves staff and clients better than too much closeness, which afterwards is suddenly given up because it becomes too much for the carer to keep up. As affectionate, warm and caring as it may be, it has to be clear to everybody that it is a professional relationship. Professional does not mean cold or unconcerned, nor does it imply mechanical routine. Professional means that the carers' priorities are concentrated on the well-being and growth of their clients, not on their own desires for closeness or for being needed. It may sometimes happen that a carer pays particular attention to a person if it is necessary for her personal growth—yet it is also necessary, when the time comes, to facilitate and encourage the process of detachment, in order not to establish a permanent dependency. Only in this way is it sensible and justifiable for carers to offer 'family-like' relationships.

Being professional means:
- that the relationship conforms to the professional context and the tasks of the persons involved
- that the needs of the clients are the focus of attention and that their idiosyncrasies are respected and encouraged
- that carers, in relationships with clients, set aside their own needs, ambitions and ideas
- that dependencies are minimised.

Even though these criteria apply to all staff members, each relationship will be unique and have its own distinct nature. Different carers will of course have better relationships with some of those in their care than others. But it should never go so far that the staff's positive or negative feelings for the clients result in privileges or disadvantages. To give an extreme example; it is not tolerable that in a facility for homeless people an extremely difficult, abandoned and constantly railing man is refused a meal by some staff members, whereas from others he gets it.

Not personal standards of good behaviour, but rather a clearly defined general setting, transparent and beneficial for everybody, should be the deciding factor on how to act. Only in this way will the clients experience continuity and stability. If the same kind of relationship is granted *continuously*, if people can trust that *everybody in the staff works along the same lines,* they can cope more easily with frequently changing carers.

Demands . . .

What are the specific demands, besides regular professional requirements, that person-centred work makes on carers? They are certainly not fundamentally different or fundamentally new. But the person-centred concept sets other priorities, the assessments are different and this implies *a different conception of themselves on the part of the carers.* Not 'I know what's best for the other person', but 'I can try to help her find her own best way'. It is not so much a matter of 'making' than of 'facilitating'. Therefore the achievement of carers will not always be so obvious—which is sometimes hard to cope with for the carers as well as for the people around. If we were to exaggerate we could say that the more dispensable a carer *appears,* the better her work is. It's not what she is visibly doing that is essential, but *what she makes possible for the people she takes care of.* It is not a familiar way of working to many, and we have first to get used to it. It is also more demanding for the staff—which may not seem evident at first sight.

It certainly does not mean that carers should not use their creative skills and the methods they have learned. But they should keep them in the background, available as possibilities to be used when the situation and the needs of a client require it. Priority is not on the method as such, or on using it as much as possible, but on the other person—for whom this method may or may not be useful. This difference is crucial, as shown quite dramatically in the example of the psychologist Barbara Krietemeyer working with severely handicapped Laura (see Chapter 12).

Empathy, sensitivity and interest in other human beings are fundamentals in this work, indispensable for enabling carers to take their clients seriously, to finding their language and responding to their experiencing. To trust possibilities of growth requires *flexibility*; not to stick to what is already known of a person but to stay open for changes, for new and unexpected behaviours. *Empathic imagination* is needed to develop programmes facilitating new experiences, encouraging independence and creating space for the decisions of those taken care of.

To encourage the other person's own way means that *carers should be ready to let go of their own ideas.* To offer choices also means *to accept choices we would not make ourselves.* To credit other people's personal responsibility requires *giving responsibility away.* Professionals in the social field often have difficulty with that. They are so used to thinking and acting for other people—and actually very often have to—that they tend to take over *all* responsibility and not to see the, perhaps just tiny, areas where it is not opportune. Not only do they restrict their clients more than necessary, they also cause themselves stress. This is one of the factors leading to the burn-out syndrome.

The person-centred attitude requires not just empathy but also congruence and this, above all, makes *demands on the carer as a person.* To be willing to reflect one's own person and work is part of it. Carers must learn to recognise and modify their own part in a situation, to be conscious of their own ideas, inclinations, fears, problems, reactions and concerns and to separate them from what they perceive in the other person. Therefore it is important, that carers, after a difficult situation, take a moment to recall it thoroughly and consider how they could have handled it differently. Above all, it is essential that they are aware of how they had felt so that they can understand their own reactions and find other ways to handle such situations. Signpost 4 (see p. 61) helps to reflect a difficult situation.

Carers need to be aware of their own blind spots. Their personal life must be somehow balanced and provide the necessary compensations for their often stressful work as well as the base where they recover and regenerate. It is not always possible for carers to manage it by themselves. If need be, counselling or psychotherapy may offer helpful support on this score.

. . . and benefits

Are these demands not too much? Do they not put even more strain on the carers whose work is difficult and demanding enough? I believe that the contrary is true. If clients experience being listened and responded to, if they feel understood by their carers, they will be more content and more co-operative. There will be less power fighting and less aggressive and rebellious behaviour—which certainly makes life easier for the carers. It is a relief, for example, if a severely handicapped man does not soil himself or lash out so often anymore. Consequently, the dangerous possibility that worn out and enervated carers will become violent themselves will also diminish.

In particular, the necessity of coming to terms with themselves is not only a demand, but also a benefit for the carers; *a chance for personal growth and taking good care of themselves.* To be consciously aware of and admit feelings, even when 'negative', helps to recognise in time and do something to prevent being overstretched. Moreover, strengths will be set free which before had been absorbed by the blocking of emotions.

The person-centred attitude is not only directed towards other people, but also towards oneself. It is equally important for carers to accept themselves as they are, with all their weaknesses and strengths, as to meet their clients with this attitude. To work in a person-centred way offers the chance not only to discover and benefit from personal resources, but also to make work easier for themselves and, within the given conditions and tasks, do it in their own best way. There are sometimes situations where it is legitimate to ask, 'What can I do to make it more tolerable for myself?' It is crucial, though, that the carer is then honest about it and does not pretend to be doing it for the other person. This too is part of congruence.

To act with restraint does not imply to limit oneself with taboos and restrictions. It means to take a step back and create a space, not only for the other person, but also for oneself. New perspectives will open up and fresh impulses will be freed, livening the monotony of everyday work; to change the point of view helps to break a dull routine. This shift of viewpoint at first may, perhaps, not be so easy for the carers, but, in the long term, I am sure they will experience it as a relief and a reward. Looking for new ways, being open to potential growth, turning away from dull routine makes work more interesting and satisfying.

This is clearly confirmed by Maria Schmucki[1] who works in a nursing home with 'validation' (see Chapter 11), a method showing parallels to the person-centred approach. She has written an interesting paper on this issue, and told me in an interview, 'There is this very withdrawn woman, bitter in a way and totally passive—there is a danger that we do everything for her and that she becomes just an object. I don't like that, it leaves me dissatisfied. But if I am aware, "Here she is, and here am I, and she is like me a human being, and when I include her, look at her and talk to her, then she sometimes looks at me too", something happens and somehow we meet each other, and I am much more satisfied with my work. If I can find access to a person, if a relationship comes into being, this is very rewarding for me too.'

Harry Hulskers, whose task as hospital consultant, among others, is to convey humanistic care concepts to the nurses, in our interview reports a similar experience: 'Nursing care gets more alive, and work is experienced as more interesting. It is not satisfying just to connect patients with diagnosis and surgery.'

Often professionals express their concern that in daily routine there is no time to work this way. This is a fallacy. *To work in a person-centred way does not take more time, but probably will, in the end, save time.* To be listened to for a minute is for the client as well as for the carer, of more use than the carer being half-present for fifteen minutes with his mind already on the next duty. Infinite time and energy is consumed by misunderstandings and useless power fights. To concentrate fully on a person for a moment, and then to turn fully to the other task for a moment, does not take more time, but requires working differently with the available time. Responding to a person takes priority over chores, which may as well be done tomorrow or for once a little less carefully than usual.

'For instance,' says Maria Schmucki, 'it is not necessary in a nursing home to completely wash an elderly person every day. If somebody really wants that, it makes sense. But most people don't want it. And it takes so much time and energy. The personal hygiene may easily be spread over different days, and perhaps they can get a bath or a shower from time to time and every day what they really need. This gives us a lot of time.'

And she realises how essential her inner attitude is: 'If I can be calm then I can make space for it. It works, it changes something, and it is effective. I should not let myself be rushed. If I am calm and relaxed, I can perceive much better what is going on around me and respond to the other person more adequately. At first I adjusted and

1. Schmucki, 1994.

let myself be rushed. But then I started to do my work in a way I thought was good, and it was amazing how at once everything was far more relaxed, I got through with everything and did not need more time. I worked with a different attitude. This caused such a calming down and was much more satisfying. I got a lot out for myself by working this way. And it was the same for other colleagues who tried it too.'

Relaxed, motivated staff and contented clients are also a benefit for the institution, and it would be a good idea if institutions would support ways of working which facilitate this. How, and to what extent person-centred work is possible, largely depends on the importance the concept is given by the institution.

Signpost 4   Reflecting difficult situations

Client: H (Name)

A. What is the current situation?

1. What is difficult for me with H?

2. What do I like about H?

3. Describe a concrete situation.

   What happened?

   What were the specific circumstances?

   What did H do?

   What did I do?

4. Are such situations frequent with H or was it an exceptional event?

5. How did I feel?

6. How do I think H felt?

   What conclusions can I draw from that?

   What concretely did I observe?

7. Could I communicate H that I acknowledge his feelings?

   If not, what inhibits me?

8. In this situation, was there space for H to decide something by himself?

   What exactly?

   Was it obvious for him?

9. What was the structure of the situation?

Could this be

a) too narrow and too restricting, or

b) too wide and too confusing?

What did I observe to come to this conclusion?

B. What could be changed?

1. Should the structure of such situations be

a) narrower or

b) wider?

What does that mean concretely, in practice?

2. Could decisions in such situations more often be left to H?

How?

3. Are there external circumstances that must be changed in order to

a) make the situation less unpleasant/scary/upsetting/threatening?

b) make it easier for me to handle?

What would be the best thing to do?

What can be put into practice?

4. What could I do differently in these situations in order to

a) make it easier for H?

b) avoid escalation?

c) make me feel better?

Note: Signpost 4 may be photocopied without seeking permission from the publishers.

7

The status of the person-centred concept within organisations

To what extent person-centred work can be implemented is largely determined by the status given to the concept within the organisation. It is most effective when the person-centred concept is adopted by the *whole organisation* and *all staff members, including the management,* work on the basis of person-centred principles. This is the best way to provide continuity and a common conception of the organisation's task. Both are necessary to grant a consistent and reliable quality of care—even when the staff is changing.

Carers often start a new job with great enthusiasm, endowed with plenty of new ideas they want, with the best of intentions, to try out on the residents or service users. Only rarely does this lead to the desired results. Those staff members already working there are mostly sceptical about such experiments and the clients usually react with confusion and withdrawal when suddenly confronted with new ideas, which have not been developed empathically from within their frame of reference. They are resistant, and the new carer is disappointed. He will perhaps struggle for a while and then give up and resign.

Organisations can prevent such confusion by having a clear concept of their way of working and by giving applicants detailed information about it, so that they know what is expected from them and can decide whether or not they want to work in this organisation. If in an institution, or a school, or a group, work is firmly based on the person-centred concept, and if the described foundations are the guidelines for the staff, many counter-productive and demotivating experiments could be avoided which otherwise use up much of the energy and goodwill of carers as well as the people they take care of. For the clients, a clear concept makes sure that new carers will not turn everything upside down. For the staff, it defines the framework within which it makes sense to direct their energy and develop ideas. If people know where they stand, they can be spared much disappointment as well as many unnecessary and exasperating conflicts.

From the perspective of organisational development it is desirable that a person-centred concept is worked out for each level and area, including the management, according to the specific conditions and tasks.

What does it mean for the management to work in a person-centred way?

What implications are there for the management of an organisation intending to implement this concept? Is being a manager compatible with the person-centred philosophy? In what way are practical foundations and guidelines for everyday care commitments for managers too? And how do they apply in practice to managerial functions?

For an organisation, claiming to work on the basis of person-centred principles, it is a matter of credibility that those become evident at all hierarchic levels. *How* they are to be implemented must comply with the respective function and task of management. A concept, designed specifically for care, cannot be transferred wholesale to management functions, but has to be adapted to the various requirements and tasks of different positions.

Empathy, positive regard and congruence are essential also in management functions. Only when managers implement this attitude with the staff, can they expect them to implement it with clients or service users. However, the conditions for the staff are different from those of the residents. For them the organisation is *their home,* and it has to offer the best possible conditions for feeling comfortable and at ease. For the staff it is a *working place* where the organisation requires that they *put on a 'performance'.* The management must facilitate this performance by providing good working conditions.

- *Empathy*, in the context of management functions, means that those in charge must be able to put themselves in the position of the carers, open to their viewpoints and understanding their difficulties, and, where possible, give them the necessary support to overcome any problems. Empathy does *not imply* compromising the quality of care or accepting methods of working not compatible with the person-centred concept.
- *Positive regard* relates to the carers as persons and to their professional competence (which should, of course, have been a condition of their employment). Positive regard does *not imply* that carers don't have to meet requirements and that the quality of their work is not evaluated.
- *Congruence* also applies to the general setting and function of the organisation and to the different tasks of the persons involved. Not only should the person-centred concept be used it needs to be *seen* to be used—'the talk must be walked'.

In what way are the practical foundations and guidelines relevant for management functions?

The *balance between structure and freedom* is essential on any level and in any area. Managers as well as staff have to respect structures and at the same time need some freedom to be able to work in a sensible way. Clearly defining structure and freedom for each area and position is an important management function. A general rule is that *the structure results from the task and from how it has to be performed*—in our case on the principles of the person-centred concept. Within this structure there is *freedom for individual ways of proceeding, for personal resources and abilities*, which can and should be used to meet the challenges of the given task, with the particular people concerned.

Clarity is particularly important in management functions. Structure and freedom, competences and responsibilities of the staff must be clearly defined and communicated, so that carers know exactly *what* they are responsible for. The common statement, 'we are responsible for the clients' health', for example, is much too vague. It makes carers feel insecure and this frequently results in unnecessary restrictions for the residents. Limitations too, where they are necessary, must be clearly and concretely defined, (e.g. regarding distance and closeness, using force etc.).

In this context, *being concrete* is crucial. Abstract sentences like 'the person is the focus of our attention' allow a variety of interpretations that are often poles apart. *Concreteness and clear information* are indispensable. Again, what seems clear to managers is not always clear to the staff. There is sometimes an amazing discrepancy between their views. It needs adequate instruments for mutual information and communication and they must be properly used. This is a frequently neglected area of management. The flow of information has to be organised so that everybody who needs the information is reached. In addition managers must check that what they want to communicate has got through and is understood. Carers feel insecure when there are conflicting views in a team. Easy and accessible channels are needed for staff to get missing information and establish what is expected of them.

Though *the staff's experiencing* is not a central factor in management, by *taking it into account* managers will better relate to and understand carers and, if there is a problem, have some idea about how to handle it. Responding to feedback from carers helps to establish contact, to recognise problems in time and to take the necessary steps to solve them. However, it does *not imply* that accepting the carers' experiences means that they are prevented from adequately relating to the clients .

Not focusing on weaknesses but on personal strengths makes sense for managers too. *Resources-oriented management* stimulates the carers' motivation, makes work for them more satisfactory, supports their strengths and limits the effects of weaknesses. Yet, this can only be to a limited extent as staff *must* be capable of meeting the requirements of their work. *Priority is on the task,* not on pandering to the staff's personal preferences. However, it is useful—humanely, economically and in terms of the quality of work—that *within* the framework of these tasks, staff members use their individual resources as much as possible. *Their own ways* should be facilitated as a way of encouraging them to contribute their ideas, on condition that those are in accordance with the person-centred concept. Moreover, the staff should be involved in the process of any decision-making that has an impact on its work.

Paying attention to resources is useful for assessing the carers' performance as it indicates potentials that they can be stimulated to develop. *Encouragement* for carers too is beneficial and necessary in so far as it fosters their motivation and self-confidence. But it is equally necessary to discuss deficiencies and requirements that are not, or not sufficiently, met and to look for ways to improve by defining goals. In this context *trusting the potential for growth* can be helpful to some degree. Yet— unlike people with special needs who *might* take steps, but don't *have to*—carers *have to* achieve goals, in order to live up to the requirements of the job. It makes sense to acknowledge *small steps* as encouraging and hopeful signs of *bigger* steps that might eventually cover the remaining distance. But managers cannot be satisfied with steps that ultimately fail in the carer's living up to the task. It is not acceptable that, to the disadvantage of service users, necessary improvements are put off, restricting their well-being, and reinforcing existing, or even creating new, challenging behaviours.

Personal responsibility of staff arises from the task and is defined by the given structure and the leeway it offers. Personal responsibility implies that carers take good care of their 'instrument of work'—i.e. themselves—and do what is necessary for being in a position of using all their strengths. The crucial aspect for staff, however, is the *co-responsibility* for implementing the concept the organisation stands for, and on which its work has to be based.

Recognising one's own part, in any professional activity which is concerned with people, is also a must at the management level. On the one hand there are very pragmatic questions to ask, such as: have we clearly defined and communicated structure and leeway, competences, and responsibilities? Could it be that during a recent conversation with the staff, I have expressed myself in a way that could be misunderstood? Did I overreact in a specific situation? etc. On the other hand, self-reflection on a more complex personal level is as indispensable for the management as it is for the staff.

Even when not directly involved in duties of care-giving, managers must be thoroughly familiar with the concept, its practical foundations and guidelines in order to be in a position to evaluate the quality of the staff's work, define appropriate demands and provide necessary support.

The person-centred concept as an instrument of management

'Practical foundations' and 'guidelines for everyday work' are helpful management instruments in that they provide:
- for the staff: clear orientation about *how* to implement the person-centred attitude into everyday work
- for the management: *sensible and adequate criteria for quality control* (see Signposts 5 and 6, pp. 67 and 68).

which take into account the organisation's primary task of providing for the client's well-being and quality of life and of fostering the necessary conditions to enhance their growth.

Signpost 5   Examples of quality control criteria derived from the practical foundations

Balance between structure and freedom
- Is the structure adequate for this person? Is it too tight or too wide?
- Does it allow the person sufficient freedom? Is there too much or too little?

Clarity
- How clear are carers in expressing themselves and in their actions?

Changes lie in personal resources, not in deficiencies
- Are carers aware of a person's resources,or are do they predominantly orientate on deficiencies, like 'problematic behaviour', symptoms, disabilities?

Small steps
- Are carers able to perceive and describe the clients' small steps of growth and are they able to make it clear to that they have seen these small steps?

Personal responsibility
- Where concretely can the client decide for herself/himself? And where is the responsibility left to him/her?

The managers' task is, within their area of responsibility,
- to facilitate the implementation of the concept and convincingly to represent it, internally for the staff, and externally for relatives and authorities, as well as in public, in the neighbourhood, the village, the town, etc,.
- to provide conditions facilitating the staff's performance and the transfer of the concept into practice.

What does performance mean in this professional field? This is not always quite clear, particularly in the context of person-centred principles. Staff and management, without knowing, have sometimes totally different ideas about it. It is crucial for the management to clearly and unambiguously communicate to the staff the *kind* of performance the organisation expects .

Besides the specific duties defined in the job descriptions, performance in care for people with special needs means above all *offering quality of life and opportunities for growth.* Useful criteria for evaluating this performance can be deduced from the 'practical foundations' and 'guidelines for everyday work', (see Signposts 5 and 6, pp. 67 and 68). These criteria allow verification of the carer's performance while taking into account that in this field, *performance is about 'facilitating', not about 'doing'.* Managers must make it clear to the staff that this is a crucial, and at the same time, demanding aspect. Carers are often afraid of being judged as lazy or incompetent when apparently 'doing nothing' and therefore try to prove their competence by industriousness. However, performance as defined above, in no ways means idleness, but attentive presence—which is far more demanding than over-eager activity.

Dani Hohler, member of the Management of SSBL (Stiftung für Schwerbehinderte Luzern) a relatively big organisation for people with severe disabilities in Switzerland, illustrates it to staff with the following comparison:

'It is somehow similar to a pilot. He has to be highly qualified, in possession of considerable knowledge and of various skills. He must consciously and carefully provide the necessary conditions for a safe flight, whereas during the flight he does practically nothing but observe with extreme awareness what is going on, taking in and interpreting data. However, as soon as those indicate a necessary intervention, he must instantly become active, judge the situation and, immediately do the right thing.'

Signpost 6   Examples of quality control criteria derived from the guidelines for everyday work

Facilitating and responding to a person's experience
• Do carers sufficiently allow the clients to make their own experiences or do they mainly decide and act for them?

• How do they support the clients in coping with a negative experience?

• Do carers understand and take into account the client's specific way of experiencing.

Fostering a person's own ways
• Where concretely are the client's own ways supported and respected?

Manageable choices
• Which choices are offered the client? Are there too many or not enough?

Recognise one's own part
• Are carers able and willing to reflect upon what they are doing?

Listening / taking the other person seriously / finding her 'language'
• Are carers able and willing to put their own con ceptions aside and empathically to understand the clients' reactions from their frame of reference?

Partial solutions

It is not always possible to implement the concept in the whole organisation all in one go, particularly in big institutions where, by their nature, extensive changes will run into more difficulties than in smaller communities. Therefore it is realistic also to consider partial solutions. It may absolutely make sense, at first, to introduce the person-centred concept just in a small unit—such as a group, a house, a ward (see Chapter 10, 'A psychiatric ward in Belgium') or a department—in order to gain experience which may later be used to include further areas of the institution. The necessary condition is that the staff involved in the unit really puts some effort into the person-centred approach, and that they are positive about this way of working and willing to learn more about it. New staff members must get precise information about the approach and also be prepared to work that way.

There are four determining factors for useful person-centred work in an institution:
• support from the management
• the way the concept is introduced
• clear and adequate organisational structures
• consultation and supervision.

Support from the management

Regardless of whether the organisation as a whole, or just a part of it, is intending to work with this concept, it needs the unequivocal support of the management; otherwise the concept has little chance of success. The organisation basically needs to feel positive about a humanistic 'conception of man'. The management must know about the fundamentals of the person-centred approach and be convinced of their importance for practice. It has to support the staff in its orientation on person-centred guidelines and provide necessary supports like supervision, consultation and training opportunities.

Also with partial solutions the management must be in a position to advocate clearly the person-centred concept externally, towards relatives, authorities and committees, as well as internally towards the staff. Transparency is crucial, especially if, in a big institution, only a particular department works this way. Those departments that are not involved also have to be informed about what is going on. This way mistrust can be diminished and openness to change encouraged. A big part of its success depends upon the way the concept is introduced.

Introducing the person-centred concept

The careful introduction of the concept contributes considerably to the reduction of resistance and fear and is likely to motivate and encourage the staff. Depending on the kind of organisation, its structure, and conditions and, of course, the persons involved, there are various ways to do it. (See the examples pp. 75–77) One way could include the following three steps:

1. An informative meeting for the whole staff, where the person-centred concept is presented and discussed, so that those staff members who are not yet involved will know about what is planned and get an opportunity to give their opinion.
2. An introductory workshop for the staff of the department involved where, according to its specific needs and conditions, a person-centred concept will be developed and the training given for its transfer into practice.
3. Further training providing opportunities to reflect, discuss, develop further and, if necessary, modify what has been learned at the workshop and tried out in daily practice.

Even so, conflicts and tensions are inevitable if only a part of the organisation works person-centred, particularly if the same clients have contact with different departments, such as workshops and residential facilities. The staff has to confront and discuss such difficulties. Clear dividing lines have to be drawn, which are acceptable for the involved departments, and at the same time not too demanding for the clients. In this respect, clear and sensible structures will be a substantial support.

Clear and sensible structures

These are essential for the fluent functioning of an organisation. Here again, limitations and opportunities have to be clearly defined and transparent. In social organisations this is often neglected. There is a tendency for vagueness and confusion, perhaps out of concern not to appear authoritarian. Yet being clear is definitely not the same as being authoritarian. Patriarchal (or matriarchal) authoritarian structures are counter-productive for providing living conditions in which people should be able, within their abilities, to develop. To turn away from authoritarian structures—as has happened in many places but not nearly everywhere yet—is most desirable and even necessary.

But it is counter-productive to blur or deny existing hierarchies and to pretend they are not there. Even if limited to a minimum, hierarchies *do* exist. To disguise them, as frequently happens in social organisations, merely results in being even more affected by them. Only if the hierarchical structures are clear and transparent can they be dealt with in a constructive and co-operative way. To be able to work in a sensible way, each staff member has to know exactly what are his or her competences and responsibilities. It is amazing how often this is not so at all.

It makes things even more difficult *when structures do not correspond to realities.* Team leading is basically a good idea, especially when taking care of small groups. But it only makes sense if everybody in the team is approximately on the same level of knowledge and experience and able to take responsibility to the same degree.

Example 46

The team of a flat-sharing community consists of two carers plus their replacements for the holidays. The two carers are supposed to share equally, as a team, the position of group manager. However, one of the carers has worked with this group for six years, whereas the second has changed twice during the last year. Very soon, problems arise because the long-term staff member, just by his experience, has a considerable lead over the other, and in practice is the one in charge. Moreover, he is not very motivated to once more, within such a short time, be open to a new person and new ideas. The new carer, on the other hand, wants to assert her leading position, although she is clearly aware that her colleague knows the situation better and that she depends on him to get the necessary information. Both are confused by this ambiguous situation, and tensions and rivalries unnecessarily use up a considerable amount of their energy.

Here a clear structure, appropriate to the real situation, could be worked out as follows: during the first year it is the task of the long-term staff member to manage the group and at the same time to introduce the new carer so that she will get to know and become familiar with the situation. Only after this year will they both manage the group together as a team.

'Team management' often means that it is left to the team to give itself a structure. This asks for *very clear agreements and division of competences among staff members* if they are not to start from silent expectations of each other to stumbling again and again over differing ideas about duties and competences. Sometimes the staff has to *ask the management for clear structures* if they are either not sure or disagree about certain conditions—such as binding hours of contact-time or specific responsibilities.

In order to have a constructive function, structures must not only be clear and adequate to the realities, but also *serve the purpose of the organisation.* The purpose of social facilities is to offer the people they accommodate the best possible life conditions. The reality often looks different: priority is on the operational procedure, whereas the well-being of the inhabitants is secondary. Unfortunately the following example has not been invented.

Example 47

Mary and Walt, both over eighty, give up their apartment and move to a (very expensive) private home for older people. There they occupy two rooms, which they can furnish with their own furniture. Neither of them needs nursing care. Nevertheless, the rules of this home do not allow them to set up one room as a bedroom and the other as living room. Mary and Walt, after more than fifty years of marriage and sharing the same bedroom, against their will, now have to accept sleeping in separate rooms.

Facilitating the flow of work and other organisational arrangements does not justify taking away from human beings their entitlement to decide themselves about such personal matters. Structures like these rules contradict the purpose of a home for older people and degenerate into despotic instruments, which unnecessarily make life difficult for the clients. They will certainly, in the end, also have negative effects on the institution itself. Unhappy and discontented residents certainly do not make the staff's life easy.

However, small organisational changes, such as adjustment of work schedules, may considerably help to facilitate work. Maria Schmucki told me about such an experience: 'It was the custom on some wards of this nursing home that after 11.30 a.m. there was only one nurse present. For us this represented tremendous stress, because so many things had to be done before 11.30. Finally the schedules were modified in order to always have two nurses working till noon. This provided a considerable calm down, and we did not need more staff, nor had anybody to work more hours, it just had to be organised differently.'

It is not the purpose of this book to design organisational concepts for social institutions. Those examples are just to point to the fact that there is a close connection between the structures of an organisation and the well-being of clients and staff, and to highlight how important it is for structures to be clear and conform to the task.

Practice supervision or consultation

Working with human beings makes it necessary to question, consider and reflect upon what one is doing. This is a demand social organisations have to insist on and provide the adequate instruments for. Yet as much as supervision or consultation is a necessity when working in this field, it is often very difficult to get it accepted. The dilemma is that supervision, as an indispensable part of this work, on the one hand should be made a condition by the institution, but on the other cannot be forced upon the staff against their will, as willingness and motivation to participate in this process are indispensable. Petr Ondracek gives an illustrative picture of how, as a manager of a children's home, he had experienced these difficulties (see Chapter 10). Of course, supervision can be ordered and made obligatory, but genuine participation of the staff cannot be enforced. One single person is enough, just through passive resistance, to jeopardise or block the whole process and consequently paralyse the motivation of the other staff members as well.

'Supervision' is not a very comfortable term, as it is also used in the sense of control. Is that why in social organisations fear and resistance concerning supervision is so widespread? To question their work in a constructive way, to recognise problems and to find solutions, professionals do not need control, but accompanying consultation by an outsider. I therefore prefer the term 'practice consultation'. It is more clear and accurate, and at the same time implies that the issue to deal with is professional practice, not personal problems. Of course, these cannot always be strictly separated. Personal problems have an influence on and may get in the way of how somebody is working. Practice consultation is also supposed to make this perspective transparent, but it is not the right setting in which to work on personal problems. The consultant may point to such connections and perhaps indicate the need, as well as adequate possibilities, of working on these problems, but she should never, within the context of practice consultation, go into them in detail, let alone 'dig deeper'. The privacy of staff members has to be respected. Unfortunately, this principle is not always respected, which might be another reason why many professionals persistently resist participating in supervision. Yet, supervision or practice consultation should never be threatening, but offer help, support, encouragement and relief. It always has to be connected to the task to be fulfilled and to difficulties in working together. Practice consultation is not an appropriate instrument to deal with personal problems, discords or animosities not related to work.

It is the consultant's responsibility not to lose sight of these conditions and, through the way he works, to build up the necessary foundation for trust. In contrast, it is the institution's task to offer an adequate general setting. External consultants have the advantage of another viewpoint and of independence from the hierarchical structures of the organisation. Confidentiality goes without saying, and everybody involved is equally responsible for respecting it.

Another problem is that staff usually waits too long before taking advantage of Supervision or Consultation Teams and often only ask for consultation when a problem has escalated and the carers are at their wits end. This is not a good place to start. The consultation then takes the character of 'fire-fighting' and is dropped as soon as the worst is over. It is not possible, this way, to find long-term, differentiated and well-anchored solutions. For that, practice consultation must consistently follow the process over a period of time. Relatively quiet times are particularly suitable for reflecting upon successful and less successful ways of proceeding, for considering possible improvements and necessary changes, and for trying gradually and carefully to put these into practice. In my opinion, the term 'Practice consultation' serves the purpose best. Practice consultation is supposed to help the persons involved accept, for themselves and for each other, that they are not perfect, that mistakes do happen and that nobody is always working in the way they would actually like to. Moreover, consulting should convey the experience that such mistakes can be openly discussed and are an opportunity to learn, to gain new experience and to enlarge a carer's frame of action. Practice consultation is also a form of permanent education—another reason why it deserves to be carefully encouraged by the institution.

What can an individual carer do?

What can a carer wanting to work in a person-centred way do if the desirable conditions are not present? Is there any chance at all if neither the whole organisation nor the department where he or she works is based on this concept? Leeway will be small in this case, but it is still possible to adopt person-centred fundamentals even in a limited way.

Under these conditions, what can still be realised is *the basic person-centred attitude*. What we might call the 'respect for the unknown in the other person'—the openness to unexpected ways of behaviour and the potential for growth—is still possible, as is listening to and taking the other person seriously. Even where structures do not leave much space, there may be, here and there, tiny opportunities for letting the other person make a decision herself—be it only that she wants to sit at the table or near the window. Even if such approaches don't provoke big changes or establish the desirable continuity—for the time being they are beneficial to those concerned. And sometimes they may radiate and give other staff members new impulses to consider what they are doing and perhaps also the structures within which they work.

Again, Maria Schmucki told me, 'It is possible to do something. For example, the custom was that at breakfast everybody was given a roll, jam and butter on his or her plate. I did not like that. When I was responsible for breakfast, I showed the women the breadbasket and let them choose themselves. And I asked, we have this and this jam today, which one would you like? And one day I heard from next door that the colleague on duty asked too, and with time they all asked. Or when I had to wash a woman and she was still asleep, I let her sleep and went first to her neighbour. At first, the others looked surprised, especially once, when I changed my whole schedule and started to prepare medications instead of waking up the women and washing them. But with time they all found it was good this way and did the same, and nevertheless we all always finished in time.'

Trust and Understanding on its way into organisations

Since the book's first publication in Germany[1] the concept of 'Trust and Understanding' has left its mark in many places, influenced ways of working and even been fully adopted by some organisations.

Many people discover the book by chance and try to implement what they learn from it. Others get to know of it as required reading during their professional formation. Some institutions—among others a psychiatric clinic in Holland—give the book to all new employees when taking up their job. Others have it available in their library, or there is a copy for each team and the staff is asked to read it. Frequently, I am invited for workshops, lectures and seminars, as well as to participate in existing training programs. For some participants it is the first time they hear about the Person-Centered Approach. However, to my great pleasure, there are more and more participants who already know about the concept or come from an organisation where they work with it.

Of course, an isolated workshop cannot sufficiently anchor the person-centred concept within an organisation. It needs more time, systematic implementation and a continuous 'sticking to it'. Again and again, everyday routine must be checked with the concept and its implementation worked out in concrete situations. The chosen proceedings and instruments may be quite different, depending on the purpose, size and structure of the organisation and on its staff situation. As an example, and as inspiration for others, it will be described below how two different organisations adopted the person-centred concept of 'Trust and Understanding'.

---

1. Pörtner, 1996.

The ASB (Arbeiter-Samariter-Bund) facilities in Bremen, Germany

In Bremen, the ASB runs five small residential facilities with 10 to 16 single rooms each and a few one-room apartments (74 places in total), a day-facility with 40 places and, in addition, it offers opportunities of sheltered accommodation for 40 people. The organisation admits anyone with mental and multiple disabilities regardless of how severe their impairments are. Some of the older residents came to the ASB in 1988 when, in the district of Bremen, people with mental disabilities were taken out of the psychiatric hospitals. After years or even decades of being secluded in closed psychiatric wards, it is amazing to see how some of them could still develop at the ASB. 125 persons in total work, both full- or part-time, at the facilities; 90 in the residential homes,14 in the day facilities and 19 in the sheltered accommodation

The ABS has always been committed to humanitarian and democratic principles. In 1998 the management decided to put into effect an organisational development process in order to improve the quality of services and the satisfaction of clients. In 2002, the manager Jürgen Lehmann, after having read my book, invited me for a two-day workshop in which 16 staff members from different areas participated. The event was extremely positive and, as a result, the organisation decided to work consistently with the concept of 'Trust and Understanding'.

A project group was founded in which each team nominated a delegate. They met once a month to work on concrete situations from their everyday work, to check them with the guidelines of the concept and to bring the results back into their original teams. Furthermore, between autumn 2003 and spring 2004, I facilitated a one-day workshop with each team and two one-day workshops with the project group.

Besides working on practical situations, the project group, together with the management, participated in defining the necessary conditions for the systematic implementation of the concept. Konrad Seidl, head of the residential facilities and responsible for the quality management, gave a summary of what was involved:

- developing a working paper based on the concept and on related criteria for its application
- defining the necessary framework for the project group (responsibility, methods, issues, documentation, binding force, evaluation, eventual modifications)
- transferring the results into the different facilities/areas (responsibility, implementation, integration into individual care plans, evaluating the carrying out and efficiency of the proceedings agreed upon, documentation)
- getting back information from the facilities about what has been realised in the different facilities/areas (responsibility, implementation, efficiency, problems etc.)
- defining who has to be informed or involved in the further proceedings, when opinions differ in a team looking at how to realise what the project group proposed (responsibility for implementation)
- developing the concept further, based on concrete results and experiences with its introduction (permanent improvement process)
- developing instruments to find out if, and to what extent, clients are satisfied with the services

- working out a process description that will be an integral part of the quality system as well as work material for the staff, which is convenient, meaningful and checkable (quality standards)
- establishing the concept as integral part of introducing new staff to the job.
  (Notes by Konrad Seidl, 11. 3. 2004)

This list illustrates the amount and complexity of material an organisation has to include and consider when planning to commit itself to work with the person-centred concept. Management and staff of the ASB are still in the middle of this process—even though in the meantime a lot has been achieved—and are doing exemplary pioneer work.

The SSBL (Stiftung für Schwerbehinderte Luzern), Switzerland

The same is true for the SSBL. By definition, it is an organisation for people with severe mental and/or multiple disabilities. Being considerably bigger than the ASB Bremen, it includes 34 residential groups, three day facilities and a special education children's home. The management, the central services and 13 residential groups are located in the main buildings at Rathausen (near the city of Lucerne). The remaining 21 groups are distributed over six homes in the city and the canton of Lucerne. The day facilities are located in Rathausen, Lucerne, and Wolhusen. The organisation offers, in total, 350 places for residents and day facility users, staffed by 650 employees, both full- and part-time.

In 1993 the SSBL began to introduce the person-centred approach, offering, in the context of induction for new staff, a first seminar about its basic principles. Since 2002 the concept 'Trust and Understanding' was systematically introduced and the book given to all staff members. Introductory seminars took place regularly, in which, so far, over 350 carers have participated. Since 2004 a follow-up workshop has been offered to those who participated in the first seminar. Supervision and practice consultation provide additional opportunities to reflect upon and improve the implementation of the concept into everyday work.

Besides the opportunities provided for the whole organisation, the heads of the different homes are free to organise workshops for their team about issues, and with trainers of their choice, on condition that they do not contradict person-centred principles. I have been invited by several homes to do one-day workshops. I have been three times over the years, and it has been a pleasure to see to what extent the concept, with time, was integrated into their work.

In January 2004, together with two social workers, we provided, a one-day workshop for the management, including the director of the organisation and the heads of the homes, The issue was: 'What does it mean to work in a person-centred way with management functions?' Among other results, a questionnaire was developed in order to have the staff assessing their managers in terms of their person-centred attitude.

The determination of the SSBL in aiming at implementing the person-centred concept on every level, particularly so in management functions, is exemplary. In

2003 a pilot opinion poll was organised in order to find out how satisfied the service users felt with their quality of life. In cooperation with an organisation for supported communication proceedings were developed, which supported the people present who had difficulty expressing themselves verbally. To be well prepared for this task, those staff members who had to carry out the investigation were trained in a two-day training workshop. The criteria of the questionnaire were defined conforming to the principles of person-centred work in order to investigate quality in accordance with the concept. Such polls will in future be organised regularly in order to check and improve the quality of care continuously.

In addition, the commitment to implement the person-centred attitude is formally, and in detail, recorded in the constitution of the organisation.

The above are two ways of proceeding by different organisations sharing the same interests, goals and attitudes. It is interesting that, in both organisations, those responsible for the quality management are at the same time particularly committed advocates of the person-centred concept. It shows that the requirement of quality assurance is not at all contradictory to working in a person-centred way. Dani Hohler, who is responsible for the quality management at the SSBL, is even convinced that: 'A good management concept is the necessary condition for fully implementing the person-centred concept'. Both organisations, therefore attach particular importance to the use of quality control criteria that clearly reflect this concept. '

So far, we have mainly talked about institutions and professionals. The question arises whether the person-centred concept is also useful for families.

8

The person-centred concept and families

Generally speaking, we can say that many problems would not arise at all if some person-centred principles—such as taking the other person seriously, fostering her own way, responding to her experiencing and encouraging her—were followed in raising a child with special needs. Not doing so is the root of many an undesirable development. However, education is not the issue of this book, which deals with questions of care-taking.

A person-centred approach in families may help to make daily routines easier and help families to cope better with tensions and conflicts. Moreover, this basic attitude allows a relative with special needs, or in need of care, more autonomy and personal freedom, and thus makes things easier for the whole family.

Yet the family situation is different from that of an organisation which is (or should be) designed specifically for the well-being of people in need of care. A family setting has to take account of, and offer space for the needs, concerns, sorrows and pleasures of all its members as well as of the one with special needs. *It is the living space of all of them.* In a family, carers are constantly on duty: they do not change according to work schedules, and they cannot quit or go home to regenerate after work. They live at the same place where they carry out their care-taking duties.

Family relationships are not the same as relationships in a social institution. Parents, sisters and brothers are much more involved emotionally with each other—positively as well as negatively. It is harder for them, in difficult situations, to keep some distance. The fact of a person being disabled, ill or impaired has a much stronger emotional impact on her relatives than on those who have to work with her professionally.

People with special needs are often overprotected by their families, which makes it more difficult or even impossible for them to take a step of growth. Most parents have a hard time seeing a son or daughter with special needs as a grown-up person whose own ways should be encouraged. For them, the process of detachment is even more difficult than for parents of 'normal' children. For a family, finding the right balance between giving the care a grown-up disabled person still needs and encouraging her own way and independence, represents an ongoing challenge. They are so used to having to take care of 'the child' that often they do not realise when the time has come for the adult person to decide for himself about certain things. The grown-up son would perhaps like to choose *himself* which movie he wants to see, instead of just being taken to one by his parents. The adult daughter perhaps no longer enjoys the Sunday routine of visiting her aunt, but would prefer to do something else. People with special needs too, have to be asked what they would like and their wishes have to be taken as seriously as those of 'normal' people—particularly because they sometimes have a hard time expressing them clearly.

Example 48

At a permanent education programme for people with special needs the participants learn to express their wishes. Earnest says, 'I don't want anymore, when I come home, for my father to say, "Put on your working clothes, we'll do something in the garden." I want to sit down and read the newspaper.' Earnest cannot read, but obviously, for him, settling down after work in an easy chair with the newspaper means enjoying his evening, relaxing and above all doing what other adults (his father, for example) do when they come home from work.

Instead of saying, 'But you can't read!' his wish should be respected. He works all day at the workshop and has a right to enjoy his evenings as he likes. People with special needs too, sometimes feel a need to just do nothing. It is not necessary to keep them permanently busy, out of fear of not caring enough and leaving them to fend for themselves. By doing this, parents stress themselves too, whereas they could also benefit from allowing the son or daughter a little more autonomy. The principle, 'As much structure as necessary and as much leeway as possible', is also valid within the setting of family life and the person-centred guidelines described in Chapter 4 may be helpful for families too.

Example 49

Bernard (see Example 11) stays at his mother's home for the holidays. He loves to watch television in the evenings at home, because at the institution where he lives there is no opportunity to do so. His mother has to go out for a couple of hours. She is in a hurry and does not want to upset Bernard. Therefore she does not tell him that she is leaving. She knows he will stay in front of the television set unless somebody calls him away. Besides, his younger sister Alma is at home too and she goes to her room in the basement. She does not tell Bernard where she is either, because she knows for sure that he is upstairs watching television and will not move unless he is asked to. But, for some reason, Bernard comes down and finds the living room empty. He goes wild and screams. Hearing him, Alma rushes to the living room. She panics, not knowing how to calm him down. Suddenly she remembers that he likes to take a bath and that this, in the past, had often had a soothing effect on him. So she prepares him a bath, but he resists and struggles even more, splashing water all over the place. Desperately, Alma phones her older sister for help. Together, with great difficulty, they manage to calm Bernard down.

By respecting some of the guidelines described below, this critical situation, or at least its escalation, could have been avoided.

Don't let your guide be what you already know. Bernard's mother knows that Bernard, once he is watching television, does not move until somebody goes and gets him. She acts according to this knowledge, not considering that he could, for once, behave differently.

Clear information. In order to avoid long explanations and the possibility of his protest, she does not tell him that she is going out. Nor does his sister tell him where she is. For Bernard, the situation is not clear at all; he just realises that nobody is there and panics. If he had had clear information, he probably would have grumbled at first about his mother leaving, but then come to terms with the situation. And if he had also known where to find his sister, he hardly would have panicked.

Stay with the obvious. Alma is terrified by her brother's tantrum, which she remembers from their childhood. She does not think of the obvious thing; that Bernard is upset because he suddenly discovers that his mother is not there. Instead of being empathic, Alma only thinks of how to stop his getting wild. She remembers that a bath sometimes used to calm him down. But he does not want to take a bath; he wants *to be taken seriously*, so he gets even wilder. The situation escalates. If she had explained to him, 'Mum went out, she will be back soon, I am downstairs in my room,' he would very probably have calmed down soon and gone back to watching television.

On the other hand, as sons or daughters, we often have difficulty accepting that our elderly parents are sometimes confused and say things which cannot be true. It often takes quite some time before we realise it, especially when we have known our father or mother as a strong person with clear thinking. We engage in useless discussions trying to persuade an older person that he is wrong. According to his character and disposition, he will either give in and fall silent or insist even more stubbornly on what he said. It makes more sense for both parties to either just accept the confused state of mind as it is, or to try to grasp its experiencing quality.

Example 50

Alice, who cannot walk anymore, is sitting in her wheelchair next to the window. She points to the garden and tells her daughter: 'I always walk out there, back and forth and back and forth.' It is useless to say, 'That's not true, you cannot walk.' The daughter could just accept it, or try to be empathic with what her mother feels; for example, 'You would like to go for a walk', or, 'You often think of your garden', or perhaps just, 'You always walk back and forth and back and forth'.

As confusion and lucidity sometimes alternate abruptly, it is not always easy for carers to realise on which level an older person is at the moment. The latter is not always quite sure herself if what she is saying is real or in her imagination. A neighbour who volunteered to take care of an older man for some hours a week had a good image to describe this state of mind.

Example 51
Alfred is very upset and asks the neighbour to drive him immediately to a nearby home for older people where he claims to have stored his carpets. As the neighbour asks questions Alfred is suddenly not quite sure anymore. The carer says: 'At moments we are not quite sure if it is something we dream or if it is something real, right Alfred?' Alfred relaxes and nods. The neighbour had obviously intuitively understood how he felt at that moment.

Perhaps temporary confusion is actually a similar state of mind to that between sleep and awakening, when we are not in our dream anymore, but not quite back to reality either. Anyway, Alfred felt understood by the carer. The neighbour *took Alfred seriously* and tried to *empathically understand and respond to his experiencing.* This attitude helps a confused older person more than trying to explain to her—mostly in vain—how it really is. Moreover, the wise reaction of the carer, for Alfred's family too, offered a means to better understanding Alfred and reacting more calmly to his disorientated wishes.

It is certainly not possible, or even desirable, to design family life by means of a concept. Yet the examples demonstrate that, for families who have to take care of a member with special needs, the person-centred approach offers some helpful guidelines worth trying.

9
Pre-therapy[1]

The concept of pre-therapy, developed by the American psychologist Garry Prouty, is one of the most important evolutions of the person-centred approach. Prouty, in an impressive way, defeats the frequently raised objection that this approach would not work with severely mentally disabled persons. It is with such clients that Prouty has been remarkably successful with his therapeutic concept. Yet pre-therapy is not only a useful instrument for psychotherapists, but also very helpful in the care-taking of so called 'contact-impaired' clients. Pre-therapy is an example of how, to put the person-centred attitude into practice when working with severely disabled people. Therefore this chapter will give a short summary of this concept.

Pre-therapy makes it possible to approach people who—due to mental disabilities, long-term hospitalisation or mental disease—are hardly, or not at all, able to be in contact with the world around them, who live withdrawn into themselves and express themselves in 'bizarre' and 'unintelligible' ways; persons who are usually labelled as 'not reachable by therapy' or even 'not capable of contact'.

Prouty's concept of Pre-therapy is based on many years of experience with such clients—many of them 'dual diagnosed' as being mentally disabled *and* mentally ill. Pre-therapy is founded on client-centred fundamentals and allows, by carefully listening to, looking at, 'feeling into' and taking seriously the other person, a better understanding of them and their world. Pre-therapy has two possible outcomes:

1. It leads to a genuine psychotherapeutic process where the roots of the isolation or of the hallucination can be reached and traumatic experiences processed and integrated.
2. It does not lead to an actual psychotherapeutic process but to considerable improvements of the client's daily life. Clients are more in contact with the world around them, and more capable of participating in educational and recreational programmes, which before had seemed out of reach. Perhaps they can visit more frequently with their families, because they don't raise so much tension any more. In other words their freedom for action gets enlarged and their life quality improves.

At first, Prouty intuitively made contact with these reclusive and hardly accessible people. Later he began to think about *how* he responded to those clients and to consider

1. Prouty, 1994; Prouty, Van Werde and Pörtner, 1998, 2002; Sanders, 2007.

methodical and theoretical aspects of his way of working. Prouty uses the expression 'to bridge in', as we need to *build a bridge into the world of the client.* Pre-therapy is a methodical instrument to build such bridges.

The method . . .

. . . is based on *reflections,* aimed at facilitating contact on different levels. *Contact reflections,* as Prouty calls them, embrace five different ways of responding to the client.

1. Situational reflections ...

...(in another form previously mentioned in the context of guidelines for everyday work), help to establish *reality contact.* They refer to simple things in the immediate environment: 'We are sitting at the table', 'The lights are on', 'It's hot today', 'The room is big', 'We are both very quiet today', 'You play with the pencil'. These reflections refer to simple things within the client's field of perception.

Example 52[2]

"Mr X was a 22-year-old paranoid schizophrenic who was very withdrawn, hardly ever speaking to other people. One day the therapist noticed that he was carrying two large batteries in his rear pocket.
He situationally reflected, saying, 'You've got two batteries in your pocket.'
The client responded by saying that he carried the batteries to help keep 'charged contact with girls'. By continuing to reflect this delusional material the therapist was able to reach some of the patient's feelings of loneliness."

2. Body reflections ...

... aim to stimulate a person's contact with herself, with her body: 'you're slumping in your chair', 'you're leaning on your arms', 'your feet are dangling', etc.

Example 53

"N was a withdrawn, resentful, deeply infantile and regressive retardate who wouldn't function at her work station. Not infrequently, during sessions, she would act out her hostility by seductively sprawling her body on the therapist's desk.
The therapist responded by body reflecting, saying, 'You're lying on my desk . . . You're crawling on the desk'.
This body reflecting would heighten her awareness of her seduction, bringing a smile to her face. The therapist could then reflect her smile and carefully try to verbalise the feeling coming with it."

---

2. All the following examples are quotes from Prouty (1976). They have been chosen for their ability to illustrate the method clearly, even if the terminology is dated. See also the comments on the use of language on p. 2.

With people who are not able to respond to verbal communication, it may also be helpful for the therapist to *literally reflect with her body* the client's attitudes or movements. Yet this has to be done very carefully and gently, and it should never be a 'parroting', but a 'feeling into' the posture of the other person in order to understand better how she is feeling.

Example 54

"T, who was diagnosed alternately as brain damaged and/or schizophrenic, used to come into the therapy room, say nothing and spread himself out like a board on two chairs in a type of catatonic rigidity.

Initially the therapist reflected, saying, 'You're lying on the chairs ... You are stiff and straight.'

After several sessions of repeatedly doing this, T would respond by making circular motions with his arms and hands—drawing circles in the air.

The therapist then reflected the motions of his arms and hands by copying with his arms and hands and by saying repeatedly, 'You're making circles in the air with your arms.'

T eventually began to emit word-like utterances which the therapist then could reflect."

3. Facial reflections …

… stimulate a person's contact with her own feelings, for example, 'You seem sad', 'You're frowning', 'You're smiling'. Mentally disabled or psychotic people often feel something, but out of fear or resignation or because of lack of confidence, do not dare to express it. Sometimes, they cannot even recognise their feelings as something belonging to themselves. To reflect their facial expression may facilitate this contact with their feelings and, at the same time, make them experience that their feelings are a perceivable human experience in which another person can participate.

Example 55

"B was a retarded schizophrenic, mostly non-verbal, who had never shown any feeling with the therapist. One day the client brought a newspaper clipping illustrating an elephant that had escaped from the local zoo. The client didn't speak verbally, but smiled happily about the clipping.

Responding to the smile, the therapist reflected the happy feeling in the youngster's face saying, 'You're happy about the elephant,' and 'You like animals.'

The response was a very solid head nodding, and the therapist knew the youngster had learned she was someone to have feeling with."

4. Word for word reflections …

… establish contact with others and are particularly useful with persons who have language difficulties. Perhaps they just utter a jumble of nearly inaudible, incoherent or unintelligible scraps of words or sounds where an understandable word or a coherent sentence emerges only sporadically. In this context there are two possibilities for word for word reflections:

i) the therapist reflects the occasional words or sounds that are understandable and coherent, or

ii) the therapist literally reflects sounds or words that are not understandable but obviously have more emotional content.

For people who desperately try to express themselves, it means a lot to experience that somebody responds at all; that they are not just ignored. In addition, by reflecting word for word, the therapist uses the same images the client herself uses and understands. This way the client experiences that the therapist grasps what she tries to express. Thus communication develops.

Example 56

"Z was a retardate schizophrenic struggling with an hallucination which deeply frightened him. A word for word segment follows:

Z: 'I'm scared.'

T: 'You're scared.'

Z: 'I'm scared.'

T: 'You're scared.'

Z: 'I'm scared.'

T: 'You're scared.'

Z: 'I am frightened.'

T: 'You are frightened.'

Z: 'I really am frightened.'

T: 'You really are frightened.'

Z: 'Yes, boy, this is really real.'

By reflecting word for word and precise word shifts, every nuance of feeling is experienced and expanded. "

5. The reiterative principle ...

... stimulates the client's feelings anew and helps him to remember them and sort them out. The reiterative principle consists of coming back to those reflections which had created contact and repeating them several times. Thus the client's experiencing is stimulated anew and may grow further. The client's faculties for contact are different from day to day. Therefore it makes sense to come back to former contact moments, in order to pick up the connection, to stimulate the process of communication and to foster 'ongoingness'.

Example 57

"Two weeks ago the client smiled when the therapist reflected her head rocking. The therapist may have to repeat this until there is another reaction.

Or:

The client may only be able to express a few words, and it may be necessary for the therapist to go back to these words again and again in order to maintain contact. This may amount to patiently and persistently, perhaps for weeks, repeating and re-sharing time when something had been expressed or was about to be expressed."

These contact reflections may, at first sight, appear quite simple. Yet they would fail to work if we just tried to use them mechanically, as a technique. The examples make it clear that they require patience, empathy and taking the client seriously. *'The principle is simple, but the art is difficult'*, is Prouty's comment. He emphasises that pre-therapy is not a set of mechanically applicable techniques, but a method based on a solid person-centred attitude, on the willingness to enter the world of the clients and to go gently and *in their rhythm* with their, perhaps just tiny, steps of growth.

The purpose of contact reflections is *to enable the clients' contact with reality, with themselves and with others.* Chronic schizophrenic, long-term hospitalised patients, as well as severely mentally disabled persons, live in a secluded, autistic world, hardly accessible or understandable to others. The same is true for persons in an acute psychotic episode. The difference is that in a psychosis people lose contact with reality, whereas severely mentally disabled persons often could not develop contact, or only in a very limited way. With psychotic patients contact has to be restored, whereas with severely mentally disabled persons contact has to be established.

Working with hallucinations

Garry Prouty believes, and his clinical experience proves that, in the root of every hallucination, of every autistic or bizarre behaviour, there are real traumatic experiences. In working with people with special needs, he found that, alarmingly often, there was an incest problem in the family. Usually in these cases, the family had vehemently opposed the therapy.

Instead of regressive, Prouty uses the term *pre-expressive.* It implies that there is something clients *cannot yet express.* In order to help them, step by step, to become able to express it, Prouty, very carefully and concretely, stays with what *they*, verbally or non-verbally, communicate and with *their* images.

Example 58
"The client, a 19-year-old male who had gone through some therapy as described before, began to relate about:
'Something that was there, and probably always was there.'
After using very careful facial and word for word reflections, gradually the phenomenology of a hallucination began to emerge. Tape recorded descriptions report the client experienced:
'a picture with feelings in it—like a painting only with feelings in it'
'big, purple, orange and yellow.'
With gentle acceptance by the therapist and continued verbal reiteration of the structure and emotional content of the hallucination (size, colour, shape, feelings), the hallucination changed into:
'purple, terrorizing, demonic, laughing, cruelty, with considerable hate in it.'

With weeks of patient reiteration, structure and feeling processed into:

'an orange square with anger in it.'

Additional weeks of structural and feeling reiteration, and the hallucination evolved into a:

'woman with orange hair—who looks pretty mean.'

Finally, with persistent reiteration of image, structure and feelings, the orange-haired woman processed into a nun school teacher who had beaten the youngster with a yard-stick. At this time the hallucination process ceased. By reflecting the structural-phenomenological properties and associated feelings, the hallucination was experientially processed back to its early trauma.

The described therapy process happened within about 18 months."

Prouty persistently stays with the phenomenon, with the image, the shape and the colour of the hallucination. The spatial dimension of the hallucination is another meaningful aspect he carefully pays attention to. Hallucinations have to be seen as a part of the client's reality and taken seriously. If this does not happen, the client will be more and more cut off from his emotional process.

Prouty describes hallucinations as *pre-symbolic.* The image is there, yet its meaning cannot be understood, by either the therapist or the client. Therapy here means going with the client step by step into this scary place until the symbolic meaning reveals itself and the traumatic experience becomes visible. Then the experience has to be carefully integrated into the self. To follow the client in this process, as far as into the abyss, is highly demanding for a therapist. It requires not only professional skills, but the whole person.

Of course, it is not always, or even very rarely, possible to reveal the meaning of hallucination or to penetrate to the core of isolation. But to approach a client not as 'mad', but as a person whose strange behaviour for her has a meaning and symbolises concrete experiences, though we cannot understand it, has in itself a therapeutic value. This is true not only for the therapy session, but also in daily life.

Applications in daily life

It is important for Garry Prouty to make known his approach to staff working in different areas of psychiatric hospitals and institutions for people with special needs. At a psychiatric hospital in Ghent, Belgium, for example, the psychologist Dion Van Werde runs a ward entirely based on the concept of pre-therapy (see Chapter 9). In the US, some years ago, Garry Prouty had initiated a two-year training programme for 'para-professionals', as he calls them. These people were taught to try in everyday situations to stimulate the clients' contact functions in the described way.

For example, on the way to the shower a facilitator may say: 'We walk through the hall. I open the door. You undress. The water is warm. You splash the water. You laugh.' Or accompanying the person on a walk: 'We walk side by side. We take big steps. You hold my arm' etc. One of Prouty's students created a game with contact reflections as a recreation activity for children with special needs. Its purpose was to provide fun for the children, but at the same time, in a playful way, to foster their contact functions.

There are many other possible ways of imagining how contact reflections could be used in daily life; for example, with confused older people. There is freedom for carers' creativity, on condition, however, that any form of application is based on an attitude of empathy, acceptance and congruence and never appears disrespectful. Applications in daily life are aimed *at developing and reinforcing the clients' contact functions*, not criticising their behaviour.

The effects of Prouty's pre-therapy have been proved in several empirical research projects and described in various publications[3]. Prouty's approach has spread to Europe. It has considerably developed in Belgium, where two psychiatric hospitals have had pre-therapy programmes going on for many years[4]. Pre-therapy has been taken up also in Italy and the Netherlands, as well as in Germany where since 1992 Prouty has taught several seminars, and where recently, some institutions have begun to integrate pre-therapy. In September 1995 the Pre-therapy International Network,[5] based in Ghent, was founded, with the purpose of facilitating exchange and co-ordination between the different countries and developing a consistent training concept.
☐

---

3. See texts listed in References section, p. 117–119.

4. Prouty, Van Werde and Pörtner, 1998.

5. The PT Network still gathers each year in the autumn at Psychiatric Ziekenhuis Sint-Camillus, St-Denijs Westrem, Ghent, Belgium (dion.vanwerde@sint-camillus.be), to exchange experiences, projects and new developments, applications and translations towards different populations and settings. Its aim is to foster the teaching, application and research of Pre-Therapy. Each year, appr. 25 members from different European countries join the Meeting. We think it is fair to say that Pre-Therapy has become almost exclusively a European phenomenon at this point. For more information see, http://www.pce-europe.org/Pretherapy03-5.doc

10
The person-centred approach in different professional fields

Included here are three examples from different countries and different professional fields which will demonstrate how person-centred fundamentals can be transferred into different fields, and stimulate readers to think about how, in their own field of activity, a person-centred way of working could be realised.

A psychiatric ward in Belgium

At the psychiatric hospital 'Kliniek Saint-Camillus' in Ghent, the psychologist Dion Van Werde[1] has set up a ward entirely based on pre-therapeutic principles. It is an open ward which admits up to twenty patients with different forms of psychotic disorders, on condition that they are capable of coping with an open ward (not acutely suicidal, for example, or constantly running away), to participate to some degree in the ward activities (for example the weekly ward meeting) and to take over minor duties.

Van Werde defines the way they work on this ward as 'person-centred and reality-oriented'. Nurses try to be empathic with the patients' experiencing instead of interpreting or judging their behaviour. The central issue is to restore and reinforce contact. Stimulating and fostering the patients' contact functions is not left to the psychologist, nor limited to therapy hours, but sets the tone of the ward's daily life. Van Werde works from the fact that nurses are around patients day and night and thus have innumerable contact points to pick up. Nurses use contact reflections as a helpful way to meet patients in *their* world and to establish contact. Even the cleaning team is encouraged to stimulate contact by not just silently doing their work, but telling the patients what they are doing, for example: 'I have to wipe the floor now.' This also may contribute to helping patients to get into contact with the immediate reality around them.

Prouty did several seminars at the clinic and the staff was given a basic training in principles of pre-therapy. Van Werde helped to deepen and develop the staff's knowledge by advising and supporting them in how to transfer the concept into the ward's daily life.

---

1. Prouty, Van Werde and Pörtner, 1998.

The nurses try—wherever it is possible and not interfering with their responsibilities for the ward as a whole—to reflect the psychotic behaviour of the patients. This means that nurses respond to the patients as much as possible, but at the same time accept and take into account, as part of reality, the rules and circumstances of the ward. 'In everyday ward-life, we continuously try to make the bridge between these two fields of interest. For example, yelling or lying down on the floor can be very meaningful within someone's psychotherapeutic process, but incompatible with the house-rules of the ward. We could make a bridge, first by reflecting the yelling and the facial expressions that go with it, and then by limiting or stop the yelling, whenever it is too loud and too disturbing for the other patients of the ward.'[2] Such 'bridges' meet one of the essential imperatives of the person-centred concept described above of finding an adequate balance between structure and freedom.

The following is an example of the use of contact reflections in an everyday situation:[3]

'Christiane walks into the nurses' office, stands still and stares straight ahead. She is obviously in a kind of closed, locked-up position, but nevertheless she has come to the office or to the nurses. Instead of immediately telling her to go back to her room or instructing her first to knock on the door and then come in, one of the nurses empathically reflects what is happening, 'You are standing in the office,' (situational reflection); 'You look in the direction of the window,' (situational reflection); 'You are staring,' (facial reflection). These reflections seem to enable Christiane to contact her feelings and free herself from whatever had been on her mind in a way that she could not master. She now says, 'I am afraid that my mother is going to die!' Then she turns around and walks towards the living room. The semi-psychotic mood is processed and she is once again in control of herself. She thus becomes able to feel and to communicate in a congruent way and does not ask for further attention. She can take care of herself once again even though the intervention is short and technically simple.'

By empathically reflecting the situation and the facial expression a piece of 'normality' is established and further escalation avoided. 'We react quite normally, also to bizarre elements', Dion Van Werde said in a conversation we had together—corresponding to the principle 'work from normality' as I described in the 'guidelines for everyday work' (see Chapter 4).

'To be in contact means to limit psychosis', says Van Werde, 'and to realise, "Today I am sad," means to perceive, "I am not totally psychotic, I am also sad."' In order to be in contact, we need to perceive. Therefore, on the ward, they try to reinforce the patients' sense of perception in various ways and on different levels.

For example, in a group meeting, the patients were asked to say which noises they heard. They named birds singing in the park, traffic on the road, steps in the

---

2. Van Werde, 1993, 1995.
3. Van Werde, 1994.

corridor, the clatter of dishes, 'the voice of my father'. The team responds to that; suddenly a patient hears his father's voice, which the others don't hear, but he also hears the traffic noises which the others do hear. This difference is pointed to: there is a common reality and an individual reality. The patient has perceived both: his inner voice and the traffic noise. This means he is not *just* psychotic, he also perceives real noises. It is very important for Van Werde to encourage the strong and healthy parts in a person. If patients feel more grounded, more anchored, they will be better able to come to terms with their psychotic parts. Van Werde compares their condition to a tree, which has a big and rampant crown, but only very weak roots. 'We have to work on the roots, not basically cut the crown, or always just work on the crown,' says Van Werde. It is a beautiful image to illustrate the person-centred assumption that any delusion, any behaviour, as 'crazy' as it might be, for the involved person has a meaning, in the sense of Prouty's notion of 'pre-expressive' (see p. 86). The point is not to eliminate it by therapy but, together with the patient, to try to approach its meaning and to find other and better ways to live with it.

The weekly ward meeting for patients and staff, chaired by Van Werde, is an integral part of ward life. It takes place every Thursday and those staff members working the following weekend are present in order to know what is going on and what the patients are preoccupied with. The meeting serves several purposes: patients get an opportunity to express their concerns, the leisure programme which the patients organise themselves is discussed, agreements are made concerning who will take over which duties for the next week. Staff members express their concerns too and share information. So far this meeting is not different from those held in other hospitals. What is so special about it, again, is the focus. 'The running thread through the weekly ward meeting is the restoration and consolidation of the contact functions.' [4]

Van Werde always opens the meeting with the remark: 'Today is Thursday, such and such a date, the time is 15.45, this is our ward-meeting which will last 45 minutes till 16.30. We are here to talk with each other. We may talk about many things, the weather, the programmes provided by the hospital, current events, housework. If you have something too personal or private for this setting, please talk it through with your therapist, with a nurse or with your psychiatrist.' This introduction is meant to support the patients' orientation in time and to encourage them to get into contact with each other, but also to make it very clear that this meeting is not group therapy and that nobody should feel pressured to make personal confessions.

If necessary and possible, the staff responds with contact reflections to a patient's behaviour. For example, 'Chantal suddenly stands up, points at the window and says, "I see them moving again." I reflect word for word and also the anxious expression on her face. This intervention seems to anchor her. She looks around, becomes aware of the group again and we can all continue with the meeting. The group is relieved that she's with us again and that a possible psychotic episode doesn't automatically lead to repressive interaction but, instead is dealt with in a very accepting and containing way.' (ibid.)

---

4. Van Werde, 1993, 1995.

The reality of the world around is also referred to, for example: 'Today is All Souls' Day.' Such references may help to further develop and strengthen the newly established contact functions. Perhaps somebody will remember a relative who died, and realise: 'I am sad.' This feeling is reflected, but—within the setting of the ward meeting—not in order to work therapeutically on it, but to communicate to the patient that her feelings are perceived and understood. Perhaps others have similar feelings. If patients can mutually perceive this in each other, there is contact. Or one of the staff members may remind: 'Tomorrow is a holiday in the German speaking part of Belgium.' Perhaps some patients realise, for the first time, that there is a German speaking population in Belgium, and ask questions, or a patient remembers friends who live in this area. All these are clues for reality contact.

Sometimes particularly motivated nurses take over special projects with a patient or a small group of patients. Or trainees do a project as part of their training. For example, a trainee tries to develop a training programme for a young man who has no orientation in time, is always late and therefore misses most of the activities. She hangs a big clock on the wall and a coloured day schedule. In the morning she discusses with him, step by step, what will go on. He participates and seems to understand. But as soon as she has left the room, he forgets everything and again is late everywhere. 'As long as somebody has no contact with himself, training programmes don't work', is Van Werde's comment. However, he has noticed that the young man is greeting the trainee when he meets her in the corridor, which he never does with other people. It has not been possible to train a specific skill but, on a much deeper level, a human relationship is coming into being. That's exactly where Van Werde sees a moment of contact for the trainee to pick up. Or a nurse has planted tulips with the patients. Every week they go and see how the tulips have grown. They notice for example, 'Last week we didn't see anything. Now there is this tiny green tip coming out.'

Another project[5] tried to support the 'cultural anchoring' of the patients. The living room was decorated with different insignia of Flemish identity, flags, posters, pictures of well-known buildings and of Flemish athletes, typical articles of daily life etc. This was meant not only to do something to prevent the anonymity of the hospital, but also to stimulate the patients to remember their Flemish identity, whether by their interest for sports or by any other point of reference. All these are opportunities to stimulate, on various levels, the patients' reality contact in a casual way and without pressure.

One of the occupational therapists, too, decided to comment less on the objects the patients were working on—'This is coming along nicely', 'When will you have it finished?' etc.—and to respond more to the patients themselves and on the level they are at the moment: 'You draw with a yellow pencil' (situational reflection) or, 'Yesterday you drew a face' (reiterating reflection), 'Today you draw a face' (situational reflection) or, 'You say it is terrible for you to sit here' (word for word reflection), 'Today you look sad' (facial reflection) etc. This way the patient is given space for the way she feels and contact may develop, with the material as well as with the therapist.

---

5. Van Werde and Van Akoleyen, 1994.

This helps her to make a small step out of her autistic isolation[6].

At the beginning, Van Werde's work conditions at the hospital were far from ideal. The importance his work was given was not clear at all: sometimes he felt more tolerated than supported. However, as long as the ward did not attract attention, he was relatively free, although nothing out of the ordinary was tolerated. The 'Contact' sign Van Werde had posted on the ward door had to be taken away; a ward with its own name was not welcome. In the meantime the importance of Van Werde's work is increasingly acknowledged. The hospital realises with satisfaction that visitors from abroad show interest in the ward concept and they are warmly welcomed. Van Werde concedes, 'Perhaps what I took for tolerance implies more support than I thought, it's just not so obvious. Yet, it conforms to the philosophy of the nuns who run the hospital to keep a low profile and just work without talking a lot about it.'

The support of the hospital has become more obvious since 1998 when it began to host the events of the Pre-Therapy Network. For many years, Van Werde had practically no influence on the selection of new staff members—so that what had been achieved could be seriously endangered by changes in the staff—but this has now changed. He still depends on the psychiatrists to actively support his work— which to different degrees, but increasingly, they do. What Van Werde achieved under the circumstances has to be highly valued. It is an encouraging example of how an individual can effect change in an institution. 'We have to be empathic also with the system, then a lot is possible,' is Dion Van Werde's conviction.

A children's home in Germany

Petr Ondracek, now a professor in special education in Bochum had, in the 1980s, been director of a home for sixty children and adolescents. His job was to update the institution's old-fashioned structures. Looking back on a long tradition, the home had been destroyed by bombs during World War II and rebuilt after the war. On re-opening it had to take care mainly of war orphans, and later of children with behavioural and developmental disorders or from difficult family backgrounds. In the early 1980s the home still worked on a concept conceived for the post-war years, centrally organised and aimed at keeping any strain away from, and taking complete care of, the 'poor children' who had suffered so much during the war. This no longer reflected modern times or up-to-date theories about child-rearing and did not meet the requirements of the authorities which had placed the young people.

Ondracek wanted to contribute his person-centred orientation to this work. 'With this I sometimes fell flat on my face or bumped into limits, but I also achieved something,' he says, looking back. When he failed it had much to do with the fact that the person-centred training programmes he had followed did not sufficiently underline the different contexts of psychotherapy and other professional fields. This led him to look at everything from a therapeutic point of view and to make the false assumption

---

6. Mulskers and Van Werde, unpublished manuscript.

that there were no boundaries, which soon caused him problems. His failures showed him the boundaries and taught him that the effectiveness of the person-centred attitude depends on the situational context. Ondracek recognised, 'There are boundaries within myself, which I can work on, but there are real boundaries too, which I have to respect.' His experience proves, once more, how in person-centred work it is imperative to clearly acknowledge, and take into account, the general setting of a situation. This, for Petr Ondracek, became clear very soon when working in practice. What does being person-centred mean for Petr Ondracek?

'For me person-centred means, first of all, orientation: to orientate in myself, in the other person and in our common context, and to enable the other person to orientate herself in a similar way. For that I have to open up and to not deny, but consider the situational context. This is my responsibility in non-therapeutic professional fields. The point here is to recognise and use the growth potential in daily life. The person-centred attitude can open a space for growth and new experiences. It is an accepting attitude, not demanding but offering, which can admit that the other person may say no and not be interested in co-operation. And there we have the first limit already; if the other person refuses to co-operate, I am stuck. Children, whose behaviour does not conform to the norms of our expectations, are often not willing to co-operate. Staff members sometimes too, feel unsure about a boss who tries to involve them, and suspect that there must be a catch to it. It is not easy to dissolve those limits. To dissolve them means coming to an agreement and accepting each other so that we can co-operate for the task we have to fulfil. That's why we are here and what we are paid for—to foster and stabilise these children's growth process—and it will work better if we co-operate than if we don't.

The details of the necessary restructuring were not to be decided over the heads of those concerned but, together with them it was approached as a problem to be discussed and considered. Yet, some of the children and adolescents, as well as some staff members, were deeply afraid of any kind of change. This had a paralysing effect which made it difficult to win them over for active participation. Then some things just had to have decisions made about them, for example, closing the large kitchen and having the groups preparing their meals themselves. Actually, this had been the staff's wish, but then they got scared of taking over the responsibility. So I had to order that this change should be tried, first for a year, and then be reconsidered for the future. This way the staff had the possibility to experience the change step by step, to consider its advantages and disadvantages and, if they wanted, to continue to participate in the decision-making process.

Another decision had to be made in order to provide steady relationships. In some of the groups the staff should no longer work shifts, but live with the children. At that time this was seen as an educational 'must'; the staff could not participate in this particular decision, but they got detailed information on what was planned and why. They were given time to think it over and the opportunity to be the first ones to apply for work in these groups. Only those who did not want to work with these conditions were replaced by new staff. In this way four groups, based on the new concept, could be set up from their own ranks. (Two of these groups still exist to this day.)'

Petr Ondracek, in his position as director of the home, did not consider control, but co-operation and consultation as the first priorities. He discussed with the staff what was going on, what the problems and implications were, and the additional support necessary. Transparency was essential for him, not in order to impose sanctions, but to find out how something came about and what could possibly be done differently. 'We should not, in an irresponsible way, let mistakes pass, but we have to accept that mistakes are made. In this work, again and again, there are situations we have no general rule for. Not surprisingly there was a high percentage of ways of working that did not conform to what was required. What I wanted, was to win people over; to learn from the daily events, to grow, to leave familiar paths and make new experiences. Here too, there are limits we have to be aware of. Like anything else in the world, this free structure can be misused; for example by the staff to manipulate or outwit each other. If something like that happened, this created a similar situation for the children as what they had known in their family, so they could not make new experiences. This very clearly contradicted our task. When I realised that the task was no longer first priority, I had to focus on it. I needed to constantly pay attention, not by controlling, but by being perceptive and empathic, also to the situation, in order to be able to intervene in time if necessary. Actually, I was not paid for ignoring the boundaries, but for working with them. It is a kind of pulsating between freeplay and confronting boundaries.'

Also, in terms of working with the children, Petr Ondracek considers the person-centred approach as valuable and helpful. He gives an example to illustrate this:

'The four-year-old Cathy, at home, had been very spoiled and dominated the family. This was different at the children's home where she was not always the most important child. Other children too drew attention. To some degree she could solve that by her being small. During the morning she used to sneak away from the group and visit people in the offices, this way getting the attention she was looking for. She came to my office too. If I was busy, I first reflected her need for attention, "You would like me to be with you right now," and then told her how I felt, "I like you and I would like to be with you for a while, but . . ." (this was the context of the situation) "right now I can't. You have to go back to the group, you cannot stay here. When I am finished, I will come to see you upstairs for ten minutes, and we can do something together." This worked. Though she was not very happy with it, the situation for her was clear. I recognised what she wanted, and did not reprimand, but accepted it. She experienced that I did not reject her wish, but that, in the actual situation, it could not be met. Moreover it was not completely refused, I offered her something which at the same time I limited to ten minutes. This helped Cathy not to make a big fuss, which usually was the next step of her manipulative behaviour. When she came to the office and the staff had a meeting or a phone call, they told her, "You are disturbing, please go away." Then she made a fuss, threw herself on the floor, had to be carried to her room. She got punished, the situation escalated. And Cathy got what she wanted. The staff did not realise that this way she got her attention, even if, for everybody, in a straining and unpleasant way.

The example shows how in the daily life of an educational institution, the person-centred attitude may help to diminish negative interactions. To handle a situation this way again leads to getting orientated on three levels: in myself, in the other, in the situational context, and then I am in a position to act. The children too, this way get a chance to adjust and behave differently from their usual pattern. They can make a new experience.'

Ondracek liked to help out, working in a group when they were short of staff. He did it frequently and always enjoyed it, 'Probably because I did not have to work there every day' he openly admits. 'In daily routine, staff members often get insensitive to the beautiful aspects of this work'. And he gives another example:

'Once, I took over the evening shift of a staff member who was ill. At the end of a day, I usually feel the need to experience community in a sense of, 'It's good that you are here and good for me to be here'. I said that, again, not as a demand, but as an offer and as my personal concern. Dinner with the groups was often like a tug-of-war; the children wanted the meal to be as short as possible, they came late or pushed off quickly. My statement had not the effect that the children were particularly quiet, but that they stayed. We did not eat too quickly, we talked, it was cosy, it was a community situation. And after dinner it became not too hectic either, the children no longer felt drawn to rush outside, there was a nice atmosphere in the group. When it was time to go to bed, I clearly asked them to do so, without letting myself into discussions. Very soon they were quiet. The next day, the educator on duty reported how, at breakfast, the children had told him how nice the previous evening had been. For me, this confirmed that, with our attitude, we can considerably contribute in creating a better atmosphere for almost everybody. But it cannot be enforced. I opened up, communicated my need and waited to see what it would lead to. I offered a space to do something together in order to meet this need. This way, even in daily routine, we can create nice moments. Also, it could have been different, my need might not have been in tune with their needs, then we would have had to handle the situation differently. It is, again, a matter of orientation. I don't mean that it absolutely has to go my way. But I must have the courage to say, 'This is me, this is important for me,' and if it does not work, I know where I stand and can adjust to the situation. And for the children it would be quite different if I was trying to impose a rule on them disguised as my wishes. Children have a nose for weakness, they sense it when somebody is hiding, and then they start to press.'

How could Ondracek motivate the staff, the majority of which had another professional orientation, to work with a person-centred attitude? Above all, Ondracek relied on continuing education, on supervision and on encouraging new experiences. But it was not easy to win them over. Though Ondracek is convinced: 'There are possibilities to deal with daily routine in education in a way that diminishes stress. Yet, people have to be able to reflect what's going on, to orientate themselves and recognise their own parts in it. However, this caused anxieties and fears of making mistakes and they had to be transformed into the insight, "I cannot be totally okay all the time; again and again there are situations or moments, when it does not go the way I would like." It was a situation not everybody could cope with. Yet, sometimes a crisis helped people to accept supervision. Perhaps I also achieved something by setting an example myself. Some of the staff were willing to take those steps. It worked well and improved their orientation and capacity to act. Others were too scared and could not be motivated. Then I had to speak up clearly because, as a professional and a director, I was responsible for things moving on. And if the staff could contribute by looking into themselves, I had to insist that they did so.'

Getting this through, Petr Ondracek felt, was one of the most difficult tasks during his time as director of this home. As much as possible he tried to do it in a person-centred way. He offered opportunities for discussion, organised case work and conferences where they investigated in detail what had been going on with the different children during the year. What had become of the goals they had set? Why had this one been achieved and that one not? What was necessary now? Those questions often resulted in staff members realising that they had to handle the situation differently. Yet it was a long and difficult way to transfer this insight into action. So many things had become a rigid habit. But Ondracek definitely holds the opinion that daily life at the home had to be shaped in a way that would stabilise the children in their developmental process and allow them to have new experiences. If this was endangered, he set clear conditions—either the concerned staff members were ready for supervision and consultation, in order to improve their professional know-how, or they had to be replaced.

Ondracek, at first, had a hard time with this clearness. It contradicted his need to work person-centred. Yet he learned from experience that this cannot be done indefinitely, but has its limits where the essential issues are endangered. Person-centred work has to acknowledge the general setting of the institution and focus on its task. 'The home is there for the children, not for the staff's therapy,' Petr Ondracek concludes.

This example shows that on an organisational level, as well as in the work itself, there is space for person-centred working, provided that the structure or, as Ondracek puts it, the situational context, is clearly recognised and taken into account.

---

7. This section is based on an oral report Rini Schenck gave at the Sixth International Forum on the Person-Centred Approach at Leptokaria (Greece) in July 1995.

Community work in South Africa[7]

Rini Schenck worked in the Department of Social Work at the University of South Africa in Pretoria, where she participated in community development projects for black communities. She found that in this work, where different cultural concepts collided, it was virtually essential to work in a person-centred way because otherwise, often, over the heads of the people they were intended for, projects were carried out that did not really meet their needs. She illustrated this by the following example.

After the elections which ended apartheid, the workers of a diamond mine could have their families to live with them. A big multi-storeyed house was placed at their disposal in the grounds of the mine. 'From my, white, point of view it was a very comfortable and beautiful house,' Rini Schenck underlines. But the black mine workers and their families did not want to move in. Instead they built, on fallow land nearby, makeshift huts of corrugated iron and planks. The big house they only used to get water. The huts had neither electricity, nor water, nor a sewage system. The hygienic conditions were disastrous. The settlement was a slum which, with each rain, got drowned by mud.

Inevitably this raised comments like, 'You can see how primitive the blacks are, they don't even care for better conditions.' Yet, Rini Schenk and her team, who had been put in charge of motivating the inhabitants of the slum to move to the house, came to quite different conclusions. In-depth conversations revealed that it was unthinkable, for these people who had grown up in rural communities, to live on top of each other in one big house. What they needed, was a hut for each family, on ground level, with a bit of land around it and connected by footpaths, so that they easily could go to see each other. For them, this was more important than water or electricity, though they certainly did not refuse such conveniences. It would have been of no use to force these people to move to the house. Instead, the social workers proposed that the company should place at their disposal the necessary material to build more solid dwellings, provide the settlement with electricity, water and a sewage system and surface the paths so that they would remain passable during the rains. As the land belonged to the mine, it was no problem to do this. Moreover, it was an affordable solution which satisfied the people concerned.

It would have been even more reasonable to ask people earlier and let them participate in the planning. This is the way Rini Schenk and her team work with all the projects they are in charge of, right from the start, as in this example.

Within the context of a community development project, the women of a settlement had asked for a day nursery. Instead of just providing it without further inquiry, the team first discussed in detail with the women why they wanted this, what exactly they had in mind and what their expectations were. It turned out that they wished to work and to contribute to the family income. This wish was realistic as there were enough opportunities to get work in the area. They then discussed if a day nursery would really meet these needs best, or if there were perhaps elder women in the community, grandmothers, aunts etc., who could take care of the children during work hours and would like to take over this task. A bus trip was organised for the women to visit existing day nurseries in the area, as well as a village where the elder women of the community could take care of the children. They could then form an impression and be in a better position to decide which solution was best for them.

This is a nice example for what, in my concept, I call 'looking for the concrete' (see p.37). The women were not just provided with a day nursery, about which they might have had a wrong idea and later been disappointed. Together with them the task force tried to find out what they really wanted and needed. Did they really need a day nursery, or were there other options which would meet their needs better? In this way confusion on either side could, as far as possible, be avoided. At the same time, by encouraging people to find their own solutions, their autonomy is fostered. The decision-making process is an opportunity to learn something as well as to develop self-esteem. For the women in our example, it was the first time they had been on a bus trip together, their first excursion beyond the immediate neighbourhood—this in itself was an exciting event and a new experience.

The following example too is quite revealing:

A patron intended to sponsor water pipes to connect a community to the water system. Until then the women had to walk about a mile to a well to get water. In this case too, before starting to carry out the project , people were asked for their opinion. The men were for the project, but, to everybody's surprise, the women were against it. Why? For them, to walk to the well was an opportunity to meet and to chat without the men being present. This, they did not want to give up. Interestingly enough, the meeting attached more importance to the women's desire than to the men's consent. The community, for the time being, decided to do without the water pipes.

Here, a next step could be to find out together if other opportunities could be found for the women to have their chat, undisturbed by the men, and if the water pipes could be built once this need was met.

Rini Schenck described how difficult it was at times to convince well-meaning donors not to just sponsor a fountain or a building (which if possible should bear their name) but first to discuss the idea with those concerned whether the gift was really welcome or if something quite different might be needed—something which perhaps afterwards could not so easily be identified as the donation of a particular person or organisation. Schenck emphasised the importance of not just showering the, up to then, underprivileged black population with welfare conforming to white ideas, but of making it possible for them to find out themselves what they really needed and to participate with their own ideas of what improvements needed to be done.

Of course, not every desire, nor every idea of Utopia, could be granted. The taskforce's competences and financial means were limited. But within this framework these people living in the communities could decide for themselves what was most important. The social workers' task was to go with and help to clarify the decision making process. It was a fascinating new experience for everybody. Again, it was a matter of finding an adequate balance between structure and freedom which, as mentioned before, is one of the principles of the person-centred concept.

The three examples from different professional fields conform, to a large degree, to the principles and guidelines described earlier. They may give an idea of how the person-centred approach is valuable for, and can be adapted to, many different working contexts. These different situations can of course include, for example, long-stay institutions (of which there are progressively fewer in the UK), various facilities for persons with disabilities, residential homes for the elderly and state schools experiencing problems with disruptive pupils.

11
Similar approaches in nursing

Nursing is no longer seen as an auxiliary medical job depending on doctors, but as an independent profession with specific tasks and competences. In the last decades approaches have been developed which point in a similar direction as the person-centred concept and work, in part, from the same fundamentals.

Humanistic nursing concepts

During the 1960s and 1970s, nursing was given fresh impetus by humanistic psychology which was particularly picked up in Anglo-Saxon countries. It became more and more obvious that bio-medical models alone did not sufficiently meet the demands of nursing.

Paterson and Zderad designed a humanistic nursing concept which viewed nursing as 'an experience between human beings'.[1] To this day, the humanistic nursing concepts fall back on this basic work. They refer, among other things, to Rogers and to a phenomenological view. The following statement may illustrate the relation to the person-centred approach:

> 'A humanistic nursing concept views each human being as a unique person who, by her experience and biography, is in a position to judge her physical condition and to estimate its meaning within the context of her life. She is able to deal with the situation and, with the help of the nurses, make the necessary decisions to either restore her health or make her condition tolerable.' [2]

In humanistic nursing concepts the patients' *experiencing* is of crucial importance. 'How does a patient experience his illness and his health, what effects does the illness have on his daily life and how does he integrate it? These are questions nurses have to ask. They may get their orientation from general tendencies, but how it is for this specific person, they can only learn from herself,' Harry Hulskers specifies in our interview.

---

1. Paterson and Zderad, 1976, quoted in Käppeli, 1990.
2. Gogl and Stadelmann-Buser, 1993.

Silvia Käppeli developed an *integrated nursing concept* taking into account bio-medical, as well as social-humanistic, aspects of nursing.[3] This holistic concept claims that nursing has to deal with the patients' objective suffering, as well as with their subjective suffering. It shows perspectives for adequate caring, also of older and chronically ill patients, for whom medicine is no longer effective. Just as in the person-centred concept, it is a matter of looking for the patients' resources and not just concentrating on their deficiencies. With life-threatening and acute diseases the bio-medical aspects are predominant, whereas with older or chronically ill patients, humanistic aspects are much more important.

As long as nursing is seen exclusively from a medical point of view, caring for old or chronically ill patients will not enjoy much prestige and be left to less qualified staff. Though it is true that this kind of nursing does not need a highly specialised medical education as, for example, working in an intensive care unit, it would be wrong to conclude that this task is not demanding and requires little or no training. The demands in this field are different and require other priorities in training. In that respect, there is a deficiency in traditional nursing education which the person-centred concept could fill.

This deficiency is borne out by Erich Grond, a general practitioner and psychiatrist, who was director of an old people's home in Germany for fifteen years. He defines the nursing process *as a process of problem solving and relating* [4] and criticises 'the lack of qualification' of nursing staff in homes for the elderly: 'More and more vacant positions are filled with auxiliaries, or not filled at all. There is no time for new staff to be properly introduced to the job, the night watch usually is untrained.' And he points to some more nursing deficiencies in homes for the elderly: 'Security, order and quiet are given first priority and this often suppresses the needs of the inhabitants . . . There is time only for physical care, not for conversation, counselling, or reality-orientation training. If a patient wants to get more attention, he has to pretend to be more helpless or more confused than he really is . . . Inadequate communication, such as one-sided, or specialised jargon, using "we" instead of "you", talking *about* the patient instead of *with him,* or communication is evasive or given up altogether, assuming "anyway he doesn't get it".' [5] All these are points, which the person-centred concept explicitly pays attention to. Grond emphasises the importance of the organisational structure and the influence that an adequate framework has, not only on the well-being of the inhabitants but also on the degree of their confusion. He writes: 'An authoritarian and controlling style of management is as confusing as a laissez-faire style', and he blames house rules which ask for 'absolute quiet from 7 p.m. to 7 a.m.' [6] with older people who need only about six hours of sleep. Or, 'dinner at 5 p.m.' and 'breakfast at 8 a.m.' (15 hours without food causes the blood sugar level to drop and this increases confusion).

---

3. Käppeli, 1991.
4. Grond, 1992, p.24.
5. Grond, 1992, p.199ff.
6. Grond, 1992, p.201.

The person-centred principle of trusting the potential of growth, can of course apply to confused or older people. 'A confused person is never totally confused, never in every aspect, never just progressively, never invariably, but always has a chance, at least, to get better.'[7] Adequate care will contribute considerably to making this possible, as much as deficiencies in caring cause, or reinforce, confusion. 'Overstressed nurses get harassed and irritated. Patients are aware of that and get even more confused. The more stress the carers have, the bigger the consumption of tranquilisers . . . Carers reinforce what they are actually afraid of—confusion. They are stressed by their power. A confused person completely depends on their goodwill.'[8] This way, the goals Grond sets for caring for confused older persons cannot be achieved: 'Respect human dignity, improve life quality, offer individual support, according to the history; support autonomy and self-help; foster relations and social integration.'[9] The following statement repeats, almost exactly, the ideas developed earlier in this book: 'It is important to be empathic and aware of my own input, to see the patient as a whole person with the abilities he still has and to acknowledge that his confusion also depends on how I relate to him'.[10]

Validation

Validation is a detailed, methodical caring concept for disorientated older people, developed by the American social worker Naomi Feil,[11] based on 30 years of experience in this area.

Validation, on the one hand, is a development theory for old age, and on the other hand a method to understand better the often unintelligible behaviour of older people. Feil describes four stages of disorientation and offers specific techniques for each stage. She points to the fact that these stages do not always follow one after the other in sequence, but that a person might change back and forth between the stages. It is important for Feil to know as much as possible about the history of the persons being cared for.

Feils' theoretical considerations are not beyond any shadow of a doubt[12] and the deduced techniques are questionable in that they tempt carers to direct a person in a specific direction. Unfortunately this danger has increased with the growth of the approach in the last years. It is often used in a technical and directive way which is completely opposite to the person-centred approach. It all depends on *how* validation is worked with. The attitude on which validation is based is far more important than the subsequently developed theories and the techniques, which, at first sight, appear

---

7. Grond, 1992, p.118.
8. Grond, 1992, p.201.
9. Grond, 1992, p.288.
10. Grond, 1992, p.288.
11. Feil, 1982; 1992.
12. Morton, 1999, p. 42–52.

somehow confusing, and are in danger of being used in a mechanical way. Maria Schmucki[13] writes in her paper: 'When I first read Feil's book, I was startled. Only by studying it more thoroughly, did I discover that the techniques are just auxiliaries. What is essential is my attitude towards confused elderly people, namely to take their feelings and thoughts seriously, to accept and not judge them, and to meet them with empathy, warmth and positive regard.' Based on this foundation, she experienced the techniques 'not as a restricting corset, but as an opportunity to get in contact with the person and to enter and understand her world.'[14]

This is Maria Schmucki's conclusion after working with one client, Mrs M, for ten weeks: 'The more familiar I became with Mrs M, the better I was able to understand and adequately respond to her world. To adequately respond, in my experience, means, above all, to take the feelings and thoughts of a confused elderly person seriously, to accept them as *her* feelings and thoughts and to try to understand what she wants to communicate, looking for a bridge into her world in order to understand why she reacts in this and not in another way . . . To adequately respond to the world of a confused older person also means helping her organise her daily life, finding out what she is still able and would like to do, and also ascertaining what she needs from us, in order to cope with daily life.'[15] Again, in this description we find, in slightly different words, elements of the 'guidelines for every-day work' described in Chapter 4 about taking another person seriously and responding to her experiencing, fostering her own way and offering her support for acting independently.

At Haus Schwansen in Rieseby, North Germany, a 42-bed nursing home, the principles of validation are seen as the central issue in caring. In 1994, the staff received an award for their 'exemplary nursing concept'. The aim of this concept is 'to achieve the highest possible life quality for all inhabitants, according to their personal needs and regardless of the degree to which they are in need of care, or of their stage of dementia . . . Privacy, autonomy, the freedom to choose, dignity, self-actualisation and legal security'[16] are particularly to be granted. Here, the parallels to the person-centred concept are obvious.

Exemplary too, is the way the concept is integrated into the general setting of the home: 'Each new staff member gets a theoretical introduction and participates in a workshop. The whole staff, by continuous education, deepens their abilities for validating care. The management team provides a role model in meeting residents, staff members, relatives, etc. with a validating attitude.'[17] This corresponds exactly to what, in Chapter 7 of this book, has been described as the desirable conditions for working in a person-centred way in an institution. If a concept is given this importance and if it gets that much support on an organisational level, the conditions are optimum to work with it in a sensible and constructive way.

---

13. Schmucki, 1994.
14. Schmucki, 1994, p.36ff.
15. Schmucki, 1994, p.38.
16. Lärm, 1995, p.15.
17. Lärm, 1995, p.16.

The person-centred approach in dementia care

The person-centred approach has, in the last few years, been used much more in dementia care, particularly in the UK, but increasingly also in Germany. The knowledge, that an exclusively medical understanding of dementia is not sufficient and that psychological and social factors have an important role too, suggests a person-centred view in care and nursing for people with dementia. Ian Morton gives an excellent and extensive overview of this evolution, its theoretical foundations and different ways to implement the person-centred approach in dementia care.[18]

18. Morton, 1999.

12
A hopeless case?

The following description of individual therapeutic work with a severely mentally disabled, non-verbal woman offers an amazing example of how a psychotherapeutic process is also possible with people suffering from severe handicaps. Moreover, there is a lot to learn from this example for use in daily life, and from the way it relates to person-centred principles. The German psychologist Barbara Krietemeyer's experience with Laura[1] certainly disproves the widespread notion that for severely mentally disabled people no further development is possible, and that the only thing which can be done is to look after them properly.

Laura, thirty-seven years old, is a woman with severe mental disabilities. Since the age of five, she has lived in the same institution. She does not speak, avoids eye contact, is very aggressive towards herself and others and, for her own protection and that of others, often has to be tied down to her bed. She urinates and defecates wherever she is. Her movements are unsteady and she sometimes has difficulty walking. When anything doesn't suit her, she starts to throw off her clothes, no matter where she is, and it is nearly impossible then to stop her rage. Yet staff members who have worked for many years in this institution remember that things have not always been so bad and that, long ago, Laura even used to roller-skate around the grounds. But then, Laura's condition got dramatically worse, especially after a particular staff member had left. She is now practically intolerable for the group. She physically attacks her colleagues as well as the carers, throws the dishes around during meals, knocks the chairs down, etc. She has to be isolated most of the time. Supervised by a staff member, she has to eat by herself, after the others have finished their meal. From the room she shared with two room-mates, whom she had attacked time and again, she had to be transferred to a small single room. This was not only to protect the others, but also to avoid having to tie her down so often and to give her a little more space. However, it is a very small room, and she is locked in there almost all day. In order to not completely segregate her from the group, the door has been replaced by bars and a curtain. To offer her some kind of individual care, on four afternoons a week a therapist takes her for a walk.

This was the situation when Barbara Krietemeyer, a new psychologist, began to work in this institution. As the previous therapist was leaving, she was to take over the walks with Laura. To make this transition easier for Laura, they initially took her for a walk together. Laura reacted with jealousy and mistrust towards the new psychologist.

---

1. See also Krietemeyer and Prouty, 2003.

As for Barbara, she would have preferred other ways of individual care than taking Laura for walks, but this was explicitly what she was assigned to do. In the staff's opinion, experience had proved clearly that nothing else was possible with Laura.

For the time being, not even this was possible. When Barbara came alone to take her for a walk for the first time, Laura at first withdrew to the farthest corner and then immediately attacked the therapist as she tried to enter the room. Barbara tried it time and again; once in a while, with great difficulty, she managed to get Laura dressed and to take her out of the room. But before long, Laura opposed again, either by attacking the therapist or by undressing herself. Most of the time, she wanted neither to get dressed nor to leave the room and vigorously opposed Barbara's attempts to come in. The psychologist, just like the staff, was scared of Laura's attacks. She felt that she constantly had to, somehow, bring Laura under control and protect herself. Their relations were determined by fear, on both sides. Barbara soon realised that Laura was just as scared of her as she was of Laura. She seemed to experience it as an attack when Barbara entered her (very cramped) room. The therapist decided to no longer press Laura but, for the time being just to sit at the grated door and wait to see what would happen.

During the first two weeks practically nothing happened. Barbara sat at the door, Laura crawled into her bed and pulled the blankets over her head. However, sitting at this door caused a fundamental change. From this position, Barbara began to perceive Laura differently. She now experienced the situation from Laura's point of view. She could not see the others, but heard the noises when they had coffee together, their chatting and laughing, the voice of the carer who sometimes read them a fairy tale; she could hear all this and yet she was excluded. Barbara discovered that Laura's behaviour actually related to what happened outside. For example, she hit her head against the wall when somebody at the table was laughing, and she reacted to voices and to the sound of keys. The psychologist was amazed to realise how much Laura was aware of what was going on with the group and how terrible it must be for her to be excluded from everything, although at the same time she needed the shelter and withdrawal. All at once Barbara no longer just perceived Laura as somebody to be scared of, but as a human being with feelings. This had almost been forgotten by the staff, which, not surprisingly, was influenced by fear of her aggression . Barbara was shocked by the terrible emptiness and despair and lack of foundation she sensed in Laura. 'It seemed to me as if she could neither live nor die, and I had the impression that, to some extent, she had given up any hope.'

For six months Barbara Krietemeyer sat at the barred door; for one and a half hours, four times a week. What had at first been intended as a stopgap turned out to be a chance to slowly, and without fear, approach each other a little bit. The bars were a protection for both of them. At that time, Laura was not approachable by language; therefore, in the beginning, Barbara did not attempt to talk to her. Silently and slowly, contact developed. Barbara realised that Laura was reacting to sounds and that she liked to make sounds herself. Sometimes she knocked on her bedstead. Barbara responded by knocking too. Very soon Laura became curious, and once in a while she ventured to put her head out from under the blanket, but immediately withdrew it as soon as Barbara looked at her. Sometimes the therapist played with the marbles she had brought along, letting them jingle or roll over the floor. This seemed to interest Laura. Yet, most of the time, Barbara just sat at the door without doing or saying anything. This appeared to be good for Laura: it gave her space and helped her to express herself in her own way. It was a new experience for Laura that somebody didn't expect anything from her, but just sat there and waited for her to come. After all, the problem was that on the one hand she longed for closeness, but on the other could not stand it. And her aggression made it hard for the staff to be close, as they constantly had to be defensive. Laura, at that time, could barely cope with anything at all. She could no longer stand the other residents and, when getting washed or dressed even a minor detail could immediately cause her to withdraw, scream or become aggressive. In daily life there was practically no situation left that could be handled positively.

After two or three weeks, Laura now and then got up, came to the door, squatted down for a moment and went back to her bed. From time to time Barbara tried something different: she sat a little farther away, or closer to the door. The sessions took different courses. Sometimes Laura stayed longer at the door, sometimes she did not come there at all, but remained withdrawn in her corner. It was essential that she could control that herself. Sometimes she turned her bed upside down, took everything out and pulled the mattress towards the door. The therapist saw this as an expression of Laura being all churned up inside and also of her wish to be active.

After two or three months Laura's condition got dramatically worse. Now, all her despair broke through. There were sessions when she just cried and hit her head on the wall. Sometimes the therapist found it almost unbearable: she felt guilty and asked herself if she had to intervene. But at the same time she felt clearly that it was necessary to endure this crisis with Laura, and to get through it. After all, it represented not just a backlash, but also an improvement. Laura was finally able to allow her emotions free rein and to express her desperation. Increasingly her crying concentrated within hours with the psychologist, as if Laura realised that here there was space for her emotions. Once, when it became extremely bad, the therapist spontaneously reflected Laura's feelings: 'It is so bad. You feel so terrible.' This had an immense effect. For the first time Barbara got the impression that Laura actually *could* grasp words, whereas up to then she had appeared not to be verbally accessible at all. However—and this makes a crucial difference—Barbara had not used words to talk her into, or demand, something, but to communicate her empathy with how Laura felt. Laura obviously got the message. 'To be aware of her situation and to endure that she felt so bad, was the most important thing.' And with this she articulates one of the main principles of the person-centred approach, although at that time she did not consciously work in a person-centred way, but used more systemic ideas.

It turned out that, just as with less severely handicapped people, it was extremely important to be aware of Laura's feelings and to selectively reflect them. For the rest, language still played a minor part. The essential thing was for Barbara to *be with* Laura's feelings and moods and not to let the contact wear off. 'There was a pre-verbal level intensely present; early experiences, her difficulties and fears, everything she could not articulate, but also her specific way of experiencing her internal chaos.'

The carer who knew Laura longest confirmed this impression. To her, too, it seemed as if Laura had no firm ground any more. In this situation even better conditions in daily life would not have sufficiently supported her. It needed an extra person to take care of her individually. The time she spent at her door allowed the therapist to perceive all the facets of Laura's inner conflict: her wish to be with the others, but at the same time not being able to. Her isolation in daily life—the lack of contact—was just one side of the problem; the other being her inner state to which the unfavourable conditions of her daily life added extra stress. There was no longer any perspective for Laura: nobody believed her capable of anything. Everybody just saw her various behaviour disorders, which concealed everything else. They had all become resigned to the awful situation.

> 'The fact that I sat there raised hope. "Here is somebody who has not given me up yet," something like that certainly was resonating in Laura's feelings . . . From me too, she had to tolerate impositions. But I could sense very soon that she wanted to take this chance. Despite her terrible despair, to my surprise there was, very early, also a glimpse of hope. Here, finally, there was room for her intense emotions, which usually were just seen as a nuisance. For the first time Laura had space. It is difficult to describe, as hardly anything happened visibly, but there were very intense situations. A dialogue without words had become possible during this half year. Laura also distinctly reacted when I was not totally present sometimes; it was impossible for me to constantly maintain the same intensity of concentration. To realise that there is this subtle level of awareness with severely disabled people, and to establish contact, was a fascinating experience. We still have to learn how to use this internal awareness, and to proceed in small steps; I was always ten steps ahead, feeling the pressure to do something. Then Laura showed me the limits and, time and again, I had to step back.'

There were also interactions with marbles or a tambourine. Barbara rolled marbles through the bars and Laura rolled them back; or Barbara beat a rhythm on the tambourine and Laura joined her; or she waited for Barbara to finish and then beat the same rhythm. Distinctly she was able to take up and imitate rhythms. Yet it was not like this all the time, but depended entirely on Laura's condition. Highlights like this were possible but, then again, for longer periods they were absent. There were also times when Barbara Krietemeyer was discouraged and asked herself if what she did made any sense at all.

The team had accepted that, for the time being, the therapist did nothing except sit at the door, but it was obvious that they did not like it. Barbara could feel the tension behind her back when the group was in the living room. By being there, Barbara somehow made space for Laura in the community. In the beginning this was hard for the staff. They were disappointed that the walks did not work, because for them it had always been a relief when Laura was away from the group. On the other hand, they also felt it as a relief to realise that the psychologist sometimes got stuck too and that she too was scared of Laura. That Barbara could openly admit to this helped the team to accept their own helplessness and fears, without feeling guilty or incompetent.

'Though my procedure initially was intended as a stopgap, just to establish contact, now in retrospect, I am convinced that for Laura it was exactly the right thing. I could not better have thought this up intentionally. *She* gave the signals'. Wholly person-centred, the therapist let herself be guided by these signals, although previously her intentions had been quite different. 'I was glad that Laura, despite her chaos, was so clear after all. I never would have found the way by myself. I continuously groped along the borders. I often wanted too much. Then Laura, by her behaviour, set limits. With time I could decode her behaviour, see it as communication, not as a disorder. This is extremely difficult with somebody who never talks. Sometimes it is an expression of feeling, sometimes a statement of will, sometimes a mixture of both. But she too was changing; with time she found ways to express herself more clearly. It was essential for me to be aware of and go with what was important for her. There was nothing I could do but put up with where she was at the moment—then she could actually clarify it for herself. I couldn't do anything for her other than feel what she felt. It has not even to be reflected, just to *feel with* can in itself be helpful. Severely retarded people sense so much atmospherically. She could discriminate exactly whether I was empathic or rather distant. I was surprised how many non-verbal possibilities we have, yet we have to enter a completely different world where very subtle things play a role.'

For the therapist, it had been essential to free herself from the pressure to have to *do* something. Time and again, Laura set limits, and Barbara had to take a step back. 'It was always good for her when I could tune into what was possible for her at the moment. Yet some of the initatives I took were important too. There were many things I would never have found out, had I not from time to time tried out what was possible. But it was equally important to set back again. It constantly went back and forth.'

After about six months, Barbara Krietemeyer realised that Laura always felt visibly better after the one and a half hours she had sat at her door, even if she had expressed intense sadness, anger or despair. The staff confirmed that, after the hours with the psychologist, Laura felt better and in the evening she was more balanced. The time had come to open the door and to extend Laura's world bit by bit to the outside. Until then this had only been possible for brief activities like going to the toilet or getting something to drink.

A big step was lying ahead, and the therapist feared that everything would start all over again. And this proved to be the case. Certainly, Laura no longer attacked Barbara when she entered her room, but the next steps were extremely difficult. Laura could not stand being in the group room: she threw the chairs around, got aggressive again, and Barbara got scared again, had to protect herself, to control, to hold Laura or lock her in again—all those elements stressed their relationship. The therapist had doubts about how this would end if she eventually had to use force or might hurt

Laura. To take Laura outside implied that Barbara could no longer just relate to her in the role of psychotherapist, but had also to take over some caring duties, such as getting her dressed, which was always extremely difficult, or having coffee with her. From a therapeutic point of view, this mixing up of roles was far from ideal, and Barbara wished it had been different. But on the other hand, she realised that it could help the staff to recognise that many things were possible in their role too. Situations, which at first, she had only seen in terms of caring, she now used as an opportunity for developing other ways of dealing with Laura and changing something in her daily life. She lost her fear of entering Laura's room. After all, she still could sit at the door again if it didn't work out. At that time Barbara began to systematically pay attention to where she really had to help Laura and what she was able to do by herself. For example, she held out each piece of clothing for Laura to put on, one after the other, by herself. Barbara then helped again with doing up the buttons. This is what I described earlier in the book as 'offering support to act independently'.

It was, overall, a very difficult interim period: Laura wanted a lot which, then, was still not possible for her. She had a strong will, but could not act it out in a satisfying way. She wanted something at once, like going outside, and then wanted something else immediately. Her behaviour was very abrupt and changeable. Her aggression expanded and, at some point, it was no longer a solution for the therapist to just lock her up again. Barbara took more risks and tried things out to see how Laura would react. For example, she once anticipated Laura's rage and knocked down all the chairs herself. Laura was flabbergasted, and together they set up the chairs again.

Very soon the therapist also refused to be pulled to and fro. Gently she pushed Laura's hand off her arm and said: 'Please show me what you want. I come with you.' Often it worked. Laura let her go and, by leading the way, showed where she wanted to go. But it also acted as a barometer: if Laura needed to hold a hand, Barbara had possibly asked too much. It was interesting though, that one day, Laura herself pushed away the hand of a carer who wanted to take hers, thus showing that she wanted to walk by herself.

When Barbara started to take her outside, Laura first always wanted to go to the (locked) gate and leave the grounds of the institution. The therapist did not hold her back, but went with her to the gate and tried it: the gate was locked. She said, 'The gate is locked,' and invited Laura to try it herself. This did it. Laura could feel that the gate was locked. She turned around and went back. It was crucial that she was stopped by the gate and not by Barbara, and could experience herself that it was locked.

Twenty-five months after meeting Laura, the therapist's work had come close to what she had initially intended. She took Laura regularly to the gym where they could try out things with music, singing and moving. Laura was now able to stay longer with something and decide herself when to set an end to it. Sometimes she reached out by herself for something, like the drum on which she could express her anger and irritation. She had begun to express feelings. The psychologist discovered that Laura usually got aggressive when she wanted to express something and couldn't. This context made her outbreaks much more understandable. Barbara could now, to some degree, risk confronting her, on condition that she carefully paid attention to how much Laura could take. This opportunity had not been there previously because no foundation of trust had yet been established.

For the staff, Barbara Krietemeyer's efforts served as a model of how things could work differently. They realised that she had other ways to deal with Laura and this opened new possibilities for them too. They plucked up new courage. Laura could now take more, and more things were possible with her. Daily routine, like getting dressed and washed, had become less problematic. There were backlashes too from time to time. Laura reacted badly to a new carer by falling back into old patterns of behaviour. But she could overcome such states sooner and this was a relief, not only for herself but for the staff as well.

Laura still often has to be isolated. Yet she can now participate more frequently in group activities like sitting together after dinner, or little excursions, such as a short bus trip or going to the playground. She is now able to endure others for a longer time without becoming aggressive. She takes the dishes to the kitchen by herself, and once in a while she has coffee in the same room as the others—things which before had been impossible. In the evenings her mood is better. She can handle her desires better and she is more clear and self-confident. Overall, Laura's life quality has improved and, for the staff, the stuck situation from which they too had suffered a great deal, has begun to move.

It certainly had been a lucky coincidence that this institution had offered the therapist the opportunity to work with Laura so intensively for such a long time, and it goes without saying that such intensive individual care is only very rarely possible. Yet this example gives us important guidelines for everyday work, also in terms of prevention. It shows how helpful and necessary it is, even with severely disabled and non-verbal persons, to never forget that they still have potential for growth. Moreover, it proves that people like Laura must be taken seriously and that it is actually possible, though not easy, to learn their 'language' if we try to understand their behaviour as a message and not as an imposition. And something else is made explicit by Barbara Krietemeyers's experience: we can foster other human beings much better if we pick up *their* signals and respond to them with what we have to offer, than if we try to impose on them *our* ideas.

If carers in their daily work do not forget this, if severely disabled people can sense that carers take them seriously and try to understand them (even if it is not always possible), there is a real chance of preventing things from taking the negative course they had taken with Laura. Certainly, carers will never have the time, as this therapist did, to work so intensively with one person; but what they can learn from her is the attitude towards such a severely disabled person. Barbara Krietemeyer concludes from her experience with Laura that it's the inner attitude of carers that is so important. This attitude also works in daily life and contributes to improving the life quality of people with special needs as well as of their carers, and to relating to each other in more relaxed and satisfying ways and reducing stress to a tolerable degree.

13
Implications for education and training

The manifold possibilities of integrating the person-centred approach into different professional fields raise the problem of adequate education and training programmes. Can we actually learn to work in a person-centred way? Isn't it an attitude we either do or do not have? Or can we, once we recognise its importance, just decide to adopt it? Certainly, the person-centred attitude, based on empathy, positive regard and congruence, is the most important fundamental of this concept. But this attitude cannot just be put on like a uniform. Moreover, there are guidelines and implications about methods resulting from it which we have to know about and transfer into practice.

To listen carefully, to be empathic and able to discern what is going on in ourselves from what we perceive in the other person—all this requires a discipline which can be trained. Empathic imagination certainly is a gift, but it also can be stimulated, encouraged and developed. Exchange between professionals working along person-centred principles in different fields broadens the horizon of our own possibilities. Existing training programmes, workshops and seminars in person-centred counselling, as well as in pre-therapy, may offer different aspects of basic knowledge as well as fostering self-awareness, which in this kind of work is crucial. Learning in this field means first of all becoming more consciously aware of oneself and of others and recognising our own blind spots. Relevant professional education must therefore enhance personal development and sensitivity.

The learning process does not come to an end with the training programmes, but will go on in daily work. Working in a team requires dealing, and coming to terms, with each other; settling conflicts, learning from each other and finding constructive solutions. The institution, by its organisation and structures, can contribute much to fostering this process. The guidelines of the concept described in this book provide reference points to orientate around. Consultation and supervision should be made available and will help to recognise problems as well as to find concrete solutions.

Up to now training programmes dealing explicitly with the transfer of person-centred principles into specific working fields are scarce. Here is a demanding challenge for client-centred/person-centred therapists and trainers to take up, in co-operation with professionals from other fields: to try out new avenues and plan person-centred training concepts specially designed for specific professional fields and paying the necessary attention to their respective general settings. Unfortunately, until now, person-centred circles, including trainers, have too often failed to consider the realities of different professional fields. The experience described by Petr Ondracek is not an isolated case. The therapeutic situation cannot be transferred to other fields just as it is. Specific ways of person-centred work have to be developed for each professional field, taking its context into account.

Training programmes for interns in the organisations are desirable, where person-centred trainers could, together with the staff, develop adequate ways of person-centred work for the specific conditions of this institution. The trainers would contribute their knowledge of the person-centred approach and its applications, and the staff their experience with the clients and organisation.

Mixed groups with participants from different professional backgrounds and work settings can provide fruitful experiences too. Participants mutually benefit from dealing with different professional fields. To be consciously aware of the differences will raise awareness for this aspect of work in general and sharpen perception for their own conditions too. Participants benefit from hints they can give each other from a different, unbiased view—not inhibited by professional blinkers.

As we have seen in Chapter 11, new challenges for education, in terms of integrating humanistic concepts, also emerge in the field of nursing. Particularly in the care of chronically ill and older people, fundamentals as provided by the person-centred approach are badly needed, in order to develop ways of caring more appropriate to the needs of the patients and at the same time more satisfying for the carers.[1] Traditional basic education in various social professions could be substantially and usefully enriched by person-centred principles.

Besides specific professional knowledge, well-founded training programmes in these fields should:

- convey a deeper understanding for so called 'problematic' individuals
- raise awareness for individual resources
- train capabilities for fostering the development of those resources
- enable carers to recognise their own ideas, impulses and ambitions, and clearly discriminate them from the needs and concerns of their clients
- train sensitivity for other persons' ways of experiencing

These are aspects the person-centred approach attaches main importance to and is highly qualified to convey. Over the past years this book has become an integral part of various relevant educational and training programmes in different European countries, This is a promising evolution and raises hopes that, with time, 'Trust and Understanding' will increasingly become the foundation of activities concerned with care for human beings.

---

1. Pörtner, 2005.

14
Outlook

The concept I have presented in the first chapters of this book arose from the wish to draw general conclusions from my experiences. My point of view has been further confirmed when I discovered, in the examples described in the last three chapters, that substantial elements of this concept turn up again and again in different fields where people work from the basis of person-centred and humanistic principles: there is a need to find ways to work in many different areas, focusing on the person and respecting her integrity. The guidelines I developed in this book apply to various fields and can be implemented in different settings, on condition that these settings are not fundamentally opposed to the person-centred attitude.

The example of the community development in South Africa shows that the person-centred concept is helpful in understanding behaviours of people from a completely different cultural background, which at first sight may appear strange. This opens a perspective, not just for South Africa, but also for a better understanding of people from other cultures living in our country. The report from a children's home points to possibilities of approaching educational as well as management tasks with a person-centred attitude. Dion Van Werde's experiences at the psychiatric clinic Sint-Camillus prove how, in many ways, organisation of daily life can contribute to help mentally ill individuals to restore, or not totally lose, their contact with reality. Humanistic approaches in nursing make it clear that the person-centred attitude of nurses is an important factor in the healing process, and that it has a positive effect in relations with geriatric patients, not only on their well-being but also on the degree of their confusion. From Laura's example we can learn that even a severely disabled, non-verbal, adult person is able to take considerable steps of growth, if carers succeed in making contact, listen to what this person expresses and let themselves be guided by this.

The guidelines of this person-centred concept are not a rigid prescription. They articulate fundamental principles which have to be implemented in different ways, according to the respective contexts and conditions. To work in a person-centred way requires subtly and precisely considering each individual situation. The question always has to be: What does it mean *in this concrete situation, with this particular person, in these specific conditions* to take seriously, to offer choices, to foster individual ways, etc.? Each situation is different, each human being is different, just as the same disease, disorder or handicap has a different effect on each individual. If its principles are taken seriously, person-centred work will never become a rigid routine: it constantly requires sensitivity, flexibility and attentive efforts in order to have the desired effects.

Is the potential of the person-centred concept possible at all in an environment where violence and disregard of human dignity increasingly become a habit? By this I mean not only the sort of horrific violence transmitted daily by the media, but also the everyday lack of consideration, violations and injuries of personal integrity happening in close vicinity which can so easily be overlooked: in the school yard, on the bus, in the family, in a crowd, at work, on the road—let alone the intolerance and aggression towards old, weak, disabled or in some other way 'different' human beings.

If we want to work in a person-centred way we also have to see this aspect of reality with open eyes and not delude ourselves that the world is full of 'nice' people. To trust in constructive forces means we need to be equally aware of destructive tendencies around us and in ourselves. Only then will we be able to counteract them. Social institutions are not islands of pure selflessness and human kindness, but marked by the same realities and confronted with the same inadequacies as the world around them.

Violence in social institutions is a serious problem which, after not having been talked about for a long time, has only recently begun to be recognised and openly discussed. Stressed staff, inadequate general settings, insufficient training, dissatisfied clients, mutual misunderstanding and lack of funds—these are only a few of the many problems we have to get to grips with if we want to put things right or, even better, to prevent bad things happening in the first place. To this, the person-centred concept can make a substantial contribution. It is likely to prevent violence and violations of personal integrity—towards carers as well as those taken care of. Violence, in the end, will only produce losers. Whoever disrespects the human dignity of another person, particularly one who is weak and dependent, always violates their own dignity too. Therefore, we have to create conditions and ways to work likely to counteract this.

This is not a matter of financial resources, but of priorities. The fact that resources are limited everywhere, undoubtedly makes work in social institutions more difficult. But isn't it, at the same time, a chance to recognise that not every problem is solvable by money and that the most expensive care is not always the best? Shortage of material resources can also be a challenge to focus on what is essential in care and to employ other resources for the quality of life and satisfaction of all people involved—residents as well as carers.

To work in a person-centred way is not a 'wonder cure' which easily solves or gets rid of waiting problems. But it is a constructive and practicable way of confronting them in a manner which, most importantly, respects the integrity and dignity of those concerned. For this, no additional funds are needed, but a change of ideas which everybody involved will benefit from.

References

Feil, N. (1992) Validation: *The Feil Method*, rev. 2nd edn., Cleveland: Feil Productions.

Gogl, A. and Stadelmann-Buser C. (1993) Theoretische Perspektive. In: S. Käppeli (ed.) *Pflegekonzepte*. Bern: Huber.

Grond E. (1992) *Pflege verwirrter alter Menschen. Psychisch Alterskranke und ihre Helfer im menschlichen Miteinander.* Freiburg i.Br.: Lambertus.

Käppeli, S. (1990) Bio-medizinisches Modell oder Patientenmodell. In: *Krankenpflegeschule aktuell, 2* (3), Krankenpflegeschule Zürich.

Krietemeyer, B. and Prouty, G. (2003) The art of psychological contact. The psychotherapy of a mentally retarded psychotic client. In: *Person-centered & Experiential Psychotherapies, 2* (3), 151–161.

Lärm, M. (1995) Integrative validierende Arbeit. In: *Heilberufe, 47,3.*

Lietaer, G., Rombauts, J. and Van Balen, R. (eds.) (1990) *Client-Centered and Experiential Psychotherapy in the Nineties.* Leuven: University Press.

Lotz, W., Stahl, B. and Irblich, D. (eds.) (1996) *Wege zur seelischen Gesundheit für Menschen mit geistiger Behinderung: Psychotherapie und Persönlichkeitsentwicklung.* Bern: Huber.

Mearns, D. (1994) *Developing Person-Centred Counselling*, London: Sage.

Morton, I. (1999) *Person-Centred Approaches to Dementia Care.* Bicester, Oxon: Winslow Press. German edition, (2002) *Die Würde Wahren.* Stuttgart: Klett-Cotte.

Mulskers, L. and Van Werde, D. Contact-faciliterend werken binnen een ergotherapeutische setting: een illustratie vanuit residentiële psychosenzorg. (Unpublished script).

Paterson, J. and Zderad, L. (1976) *Humanistic Nursing.* London: Wiley.

Pörtner, M. (1990) Client-Centered Psychotherapy with Mentally Retarded Persons: Catherine and Ruth. In: G. Lietaer, J. Rombauts and R. Van Balen, R. (eds.) *Client-Centered and Experiential Psychotherapy in the Nineties*, 659–669, Leuven: University Press.

Pörtner, M. (1994) *Praxis der Gesprächspsychotherapie, Interviews mit Therapeuten*, Stuttgart: Klett-Cotta.

Pörtner, M. (1996) *Ernstnehmen, Zutrauen, Verstehen—Personzentrierte Haltung im Umgang mit geistig behinderten und pflegebedürftigen Menschen.* Stuttgart: Klett-Cotta. (2004) 4th, modified and extended edition, Stuttgart: Klett-Cotta. (1998) Dutch edition, *Serieus nemen, vertrouwen, begrijpen—cliëntgerichte zorg voor menschen meet en verstandelijke handicap.* Maarssen: Elsevier/De Tijdstroom. (2003) Danish edition, *Den personcentrerede I arbejdet med sindslidende, udiviklingshaemmede og demente mennesker.* Copenhagen: Hans Reitzels Forlag.

Pörtner, M. (1996a) Working with the Mentally Handicapped in a Person-Centered Way—is it possible, is it appropriate and what does it mean in practice? In: R. Hutterer, G. Pawlowsky, P.F. Schmid, R. Stipsits, (eds.): *Client-Centered and Experiential Psychotherapy. A Paradigm in Motion,* 513–527. Frankfurt a.M.: Peter Lang, Europäischer Verlag der Wissenschaften.

Pörtner, M. (1999) Psychotherapie für Menschen mit geistiger Behinderung. In: *Brennpunkt, 81/99*, 7–13.

Pörtner, M. (2000) Der personzentrierte Ansatz in der Arbeit mit geistig behinderten Menschen. In: Keil, W. and Sturm, G. (eds.) *Der personzentrierte Ansatz in der Psychotherapie. Die vielen Gesichter der klientenzentrierten Psychotherapie.* Wien, New York: Springer, 509–532.

Pörtner, M. (2001) The Person-Centred Approach in working with people with special needs. In: *Person-Centred Practice, 9* (1),18–30.

Pörtner,M. (2003) *Brücken bauen. Menschen mit geistiger Behinderung verstehen und begleiten.* Stuttgart, Klett-Cotta. (English edition *Building Bridges* planned at PCCS Books for 2009).

Pörtner, M. (2005) *Alt sein ist anders. Personzentrierte Betreuung von alten Menschen.* Stuttgart: Klett-Cotta. (English edition *Being Old is Different* planned at PCCS Books for 2008).

Pörtner, M. (2005a) Nine considerations concerning psychotherapy and care for people 'with special needs'. In: S. Joseph and R. Worsley (eds.) *Person-Centred Psychopathology. A positive psychology of mental health.* Ross-on-Wye: PCCS Books.

Prouty, G. (1976) Pre-therapy, a method of treating pre-expressive psychotic and retarded patients. In: *Psychotherapy: Theory, Research and Practice, 13*, 290–94.

Prouty, G. (1977) Protosymbolic method: A phenomenological treatment of schizophrenic hallucinations. In: *Journal of Mental Imagery, 1* (2), 339–4.

Prouty, G. (1983) Hallucinatory contact: A phenomenological treatment of schizophrenics. In: *Journal of Communication Therapy, 2*, 99–103.

Prouty, G. (1986) The pre-symbolic structure and therapeutic transformation of hallucinations. In: M. Wolpin, J. Shorr and L. Kreuger (eds.): *Imagery, Vol. 4*, 99–106, New York: Plenum Press.

Prouty, G. (1988b) Pre-Therapy with mentally retarded/psychotic clients. In: *Psychiatric Aspects of Mental Retardation Reviews, 3* (4), (426–41).

Prouty, G. (1990) Pre-therapy: A theoretical evolution in the person-centered/experiential psychotherapy of schizophrenia and retardation. In: Lietaer, G., Rombauts, J. and Van Balen, R. (eds.) *Client-Centered and Experiential Psychotherapy in the Nineties*, 645–58. Leuven: University Press.

Prouty, G. (1991) The pre-symbolic structure and processing of schizophrenic hallucinations: The problematic of an non-process structure. In: L. Fusek (ed.) *New Directions in Client-Centered Therapy: Practice with Difficult Client Populations*, 1–18. Chicago: Chicago Counseling and Psychotherapy Research Center.

Prouty, G. (1994) *Theoretical Evolutions in Person-Centered/Experiential Therapy—Applications to Schizophrenic and Retarded Psychoses*. Westport: Praeger.

Prouty, G. and Cronwall, M. (1990) Psychotherapy with a depressed mentally retarded adult: An application of Pre-Therapy. In: A. Dosen and F. Menolascino (eds.) *Depression in Mentally Retarded Children and Adults*, 281–93. Leiden: Logan Publications.

Prouty, G. and Kubiak, M. (1988a) The development of communicative contact with a catatonic schizophrenic. In: *Journal of Communication Therapy, 4* (1), 13–20.

Prouty, G. and Pietrzak, S. (1988) Pre-therapy method applied to persons experiencing hallucinatory images. In: *Person-Centered Review, 3* (4), 426–41.

Prouty, G., Van Werde, D. and Pörtner, M. (1998) *Prä-Therapie,* Stuttgart: Klett-Cotta. (2002) English edition, Ross-on-Wye: PCCS Books.

Rogers, C. R. (1942) *Counseling and Psychotherapy,* Boston: Houghton Mifflin.

Rogers, C. R. (1951) *Client-Centered Therapy*. Boston: Houghton Mifflin.

Rogers, C. R. (1957) The necessary and sufficient conditions of therapeutic personality change. *Journal of Consulting Psychology, 21* (2), 95–103.

Rogers, C. R. (1961) *On Becoming a Person.* Boston: Houghton Mifflin.

Rogers, C. R. (1969) *Freedom to Learn.* Columbus: Carles E. Merrill.

Rogers, C. R. (1970) *On Encounter Groups.* New York, Evanston, London: Harper & Row.

Rogers, C. R. (1977) *On Personal Power.* New York: Delacorte.

Rogers, C. R. (1980) *A Way of Being.* Boston: Houghton Mifflin.

Rogers, C. R. (1982) *Freedom to Learn for the 80s.* Boston: Houghton Mifflin.

Schmucki, M. (1994) *Validation—ein Weg zur Welt des verwirrten alten Menschen, Kaderschule für die Krankenpflege, Regionalzentrum Winterthur, Höhere Fachausbildung in Krankenpflege, Stufe 1*, Kurs Nr. 93038.

Sinason, V. (1992) *Mental Handicap and the Human Condition: New approaches from the Tavistock.* London: Free Association Books.

Van Werde, D. (1990) Die Wiederherstellung des psychologischen Kontaktes bei akuter Psychose— Eine Anwendung von Prouty's Pre-Therapy. *GwG-Zeitschrift, 21*, 78, 42–45.

Van Werde, D. (1993/95) The translation of the contact-paradigm into a ward approach. Written for Prouty, G. (1994) and Pörtner, M. (1996).

Van Werde, D.(1994) An introduction to client-centred pre-therapy. In: D. Mearns, *Developing Person-Centred Counselling.* London: Sage.

Van Werde, D. (1994a) 'Werken aan contact' als leidmotief van de wekelijkse afdelingsvergadering in residentiële psychosenzorg. In: *Tijdschrift voor Psychiatrie, 8*, 571–84.

Van Werde, D. and Van Akoleyen J. (1994) 'Verankering' als kernidee van de interieurinrichting in residentiële Psychosenzorg. *Tijdschrift Klinische Psychologie, 24* (4), 293–302.

Van Werde, D. and Morton I. (1999) The relevance of Prouty's Pre-Therapy to dementia care. In: I. Morton, *Person-Centred Approaches to Dementia Care.* Oxford: Winslow Press.

Index

First Steps in Counselling 3rd edn
A students' companion for basic introductory courses
Pete Sanders

ISBN 978 1 898 05951 6, £12.00

This best-selling book is used as the standard course textbook on hundreds of introductory courses throughout the UK. Each year thousands of volunteers, social workers, carers, teachers, nurses and beginning counsellors use *First Steps* as their starting point for learning.

The Person-Centred Counselling Primer
Pete Sanders

ISBN 978 1 898 05980 6, £10.50

This book presents an unparalleled, comprehensive description of person-centred counselling. Personality theory, motivation, therapy theory, non-directivity and the process of change are all covered in Pete Sanders' easy and accessible style.

New *Primers* series

The Contact Work Primer
edited by Pete Sanders

ISBN 978 1 898 05984 4, £10.50

This book introduces Pre-therapy—the work of Garry Prouty and his associates. In-patient psychiatry, clinical psychology, psychotherapy, dementia care and everyday care are covered, with contributions from Dion Van Werde, Lisbeth Sommerbeck and Penny Dodds.

Voices of the Voiceless
Jan Hawkins

ISBN 978 1 898 05941 7, £16.00

Voices of the Voiceless is an inspiring, passionate and comprehensive exploration of practice that offers hope and encouragement to counsellors and practitioners working with people living with learning difficulties. Jan Hawkins combines 27 years as the mother of a person with learning difficulties and 15 years as a counsellor to produce this accessible, enlightening book based on the person-centred approach.

Pre-therapy
Garry Prouty, Dion Van Werde
and Marlis Pörtner

ISBN 978 1 898 05934 9, £16.00

Pre-therapy is a method for anyone wanting to work with people whose ability to establish and maintain psychological contact is impaired temporarily or permanently by illness, injury or distress, whether of organic or psychological origin. Pre-therapy has changed the practice of professionals, carers and family members in Europe and is now increasingly available in the UK.